NEW ELEMENTARY
MATHEMATICS
SYLLABUS D
3
WORKBOOK

Low Wai Cheng
BSc, Dip Ed

Published by EPB Pan Pacific

An imprint of Panpac Education Private Limited
Times Centre
1 New Industrial Road
Singapore 536196

Panpac Education

Email: panpmktg@panpaceducation.com
Website: http://www.panpaceducation.com

EPB Pan Pacific is a trademark of Times Publishing Limited

ISBN 978-981-271-938-6

First published 1998
Reprinted 2002
Reprinted 2005
Reprinted 2007 (twice)

Printed by Utopia Press Pte Ltd

PREFACE

New Elementary Mathematics Workbook 3, a supplement to the textbooks *New Elementary Mathematics 3A* and *3B*, is specially written to provide students with additional practice. It follows closely the latest Singapore-Cambridge G.C.E. 'O' Level Mathematics Syllabus D.

Each *Revision Exercise* covers a chapter in the textbook and attempts have been made to integrate the appropriate concepts of different topics into a single question. *Test Papers* are provided after every two revision exercises to help reinforce concepts learnt. *Mid-Term* and *Final Term Assessment Papers* have also been included to prepare students for the final examination.

CONTENTS

CHAPTER 1

Computation and Manipulation

1. Evaluate the following:

   (a) 3^4

   (b) 7^{-3}

   (c) $\left(\dfrac{2}{5}\right)^3$

   (d) $\left(-\dfrac{1}{4}\right)^{-2}$

   (e) $\left(2\dfrac{1}{3}\right)^{-3}$

   (f) 0.04^{-2}

   (g) $\left(\dfrac{8}{3}\right)^{-1}$

   (h) $64^{\frac{1}{3}}$

   (i) $121^{\frac{3}{2}}$

   (j) $27^{1\frac{1}{3}}$

   (k) $9^{-0.5}$

   (l) $\left(\dfrac{1}{8}\right)^{-\frac{1}{3}}$

   (m) $0.36^{\frac{1}{2}}$

   (n) $81^{-0.75}$

2. Evaluate the following:

   (a) $243^{0.4}$

   (b) $\left(\dfrac{8}{27}\right)^{-\frac{2}{3}}$

   (c) $\left(5\dfrac{1}{16}\right)^{-\frac{3}{4}}$

   (d) $\left(2\dfrac{7}{9}\right)^{\frac{3}{2}}$

   (e) $216^{\frac{2}{3}}$

   (f) $\left(\dfrac{1}{32}\right)^{\frac{2}{5}}$

   (g) $(-125)^{\frac{2}{3}}$

   (h) $(-128)^{-\frac{1}{7}}$

   (i) $1\,024^{0.3}$

   (j) $(-8)^{-\frac{2}{3}}$

   (k) $(-0.343)^{\frac{1}{3}}$

   (l) $(-0.512)^{\frac{2}{3}}$

   (m) $\left(\dfrac{729}{1\,331}\right)^{-\frac{1}{3}}$

   (n) $(0.000\,1)^{-0.75}$

3. Evaluate the following:

(a) $\left(81^{\frac{1}{4}}\right)^4$

(b) $\left(16^{-\frac{1}{2}}\right)^{-\frac{1}{2}}$

(c) $\left(32^{\frac{3}{5}}\right)^0$

(d) $\left(3^4\right)^{-\frac{3}{2}}$

(e) $\left(64^{-\frac{1}{3}}\right)^2$

(f) $\left(27^{\frac{3}{2}}\right)^{-\frac{2}{3}}$

(g) $\left(\left(16^2\right)^{-\frac{1}{3}}\right)^{\frac{3}{4}}$

(h) $0^{\frac{1}{3}} \times \left(\frac{1}{3}\right)^0$

(i) $8^{\frac{1}{4}} \times 32^{\frac{1}{4}}$

(j) $4^{-\frac{1}{3}} \times 4^{\frac{5}{6}}$

(k) $25^{-\frac{1}{4}} \times 25^{-\frac{1}{4}}$

(l) $25^{\frac{1}{2}} \times 5^0$

(m) $4^{\frac{3}{5}} \times 32^{\frac{3}{5}} \times 8^{\frac{3}{5}}$

(n) $32^{\frac{1}{2}} \times 2^{-\frac{1}{2}}$

(o) $64^{-\frac{2}{3}} \times 64^{\frac{1}{6}}$

(p) $\dfrac{200^{-\frac{2}{3}}}{8^{-\frac{3}{2}}}$

(q) $\dfrac{27^{-\frac{1}{3}}}{27^{-\frac{5}{3}}}$

(r) $\dfrac{3^{-\frac{1}{4}}}{243^{-\frac{1}{4}}}$

(s) $\dfrac{27^{\frac{2}{5}}}{9^{-\frac{2}{5}}}$

(t) $\dfrac{625^{-\frac{5}{4}}}{625^{-\frac{1}{4}}}$

4. Evaluate the following:

(a) $\dfrac{9^{\frac{1}{2}} \times 8^{\frac{1}{2}}}{2^{\frac{1}{2}}}$

(b) $125^{\frac{1}{2}} \times 5^{\frac{3}{2}}$

(c) $\left(7^0\right)^{-2} \times 7^{\frac{5}{2}} \div 7^{\frac{1}{2}}$

(d) $3^{-2} \times 9^{\frac{1}{2}} \times 27^{-\frac{2}{3}}$

2

(e) $\dfrac{32^{-\frac{4}{9}} \times 32^{-\frac{2}{9}}}{4^{-\frac{2}{3}}}$

(f) $81^{\frac{3}{4}} \times 27^{-\frac{1}{3}}$

(g) $\left(\dfrac{32}{243}\right)^{\frac{2}{5}} \times 64^{-\frac{1}{3}}$

(h) $9^{\frac{1}{2}} \times 49^{-\frac{1}{2}}$

(i) $(0.01)^{-1.5} \times 5^{-2}$

(j) $8^{-2} \times 16^{\frac{3}{2}}$

(k) $\left(27^{\frac{2}{3}} - 4^{\frac{3}{2}}\right)^{2}$

(l) $16^{\frac{3}{4}} + 4^{1.5} + 0.5^{-2}$

(m) $(1^3 + 2^3 + 3^3)^{\frac{3}{2}}$

(n) $(3^0 + 3^1 + 3^2 + 3^3 + 3^4)^{-\frac{1}{2}}$

(o) $144^{0.5} \times 9^{-\frac{3}{2}} + 3^{-2}$

(p) $\dfrac{8^{\frac{1}{3}} \times 16^{\frac{1}{3}}}{32^{-\frac{1}{3}}}$

(q) $\dfrac{2.88^{\frac{1}{2}}}{2^{\frac{1}{2}}} \div (0.09)^{\frac{3}{2}}$

(r) $\dfrac{5^0 \times 25^{\frac{1}{3}}}{125^{\frac{1}{3}}}$

(s) $16^{\frac{2}{3}} \div 64^{\frac{1}{4}} \div 4^{\frac{1}{12}}$

(t) $\dfrac{9^{-\frac{2}{3}} \times 27^{-\frac{1}{2}}}{3^{-\frac{1}{6}} \times 3^{-\frac{2}{3}}}$

5. Simplify the following and express your answers in the index form.

(a) $9a^{\frac{1}{2}} \times 8\,a^{\frac{1}{3}}$

(b) $\left(a^{\frac{1}{3}}\right)^{2} \times \left(a^{-\frac{2}{3}}\right)^{3}$

(c) $x^{\frac{3}{4}} y^{-\frac{3}{14}} \div x^{-\frac{1}{2}} y^{\frac{6}{7}}$

(d) $a^{-\frac{2}{3}} b^{\frac{5}{6}} \times a^{-\frac{1}{2}} b \div (ab)^{\frac{1}{3}}$

(e) $\left(x^{\frac{1}{2}} y^{3}\right)^{-\frac{1}{2}} \div \left(x^{\frac{1}{4}} y^{-\frac{1}{2}}\right)^{-5}$

(f) $\dfrac{(x^{-2} y^{2})^{\frac{3}{2}} \times (-xy)^{3}}{(-x^{\frac{3}{2}} y^{-1})^{4}}$

(g) $\dfrac{(a^4)^0 \div (a^{\frac{1}{2}} b^{-\frac{2}{3}})^{15}}{(a^3 b)^7}$

(h) $\left(a^{\frac{2}{5}} \div a^{\frac{3}{5}}\right)^{10} \div \left(a^{\frac{1}{5}} \div a^{\frac{3}{5}}\right)^{2}$

6. Simplify and express each of the following in the index form.

(a) $\sqrt{4a^{12}}$

(b) $\sqrt[3]{a^{18}}$

(c) $\sqrt[4]{81x^{32}y^4}$

(d) $\sqrt[3]{\dfrac{125}{8}p^9q^{15}r^8}$

(e) $\sqrt{(a+2b)^5}$

(f) $\sqrt[3]{x^2} \times x^{-1} \div \sqrt{x}$

(g) $n^{\frac{1}{3}} \times \sqrt[4]{m^8 n}$

(h) $\dfrac{a^3}{\sqrt{b}} \times \dfrac{b^3}{a^0}$

(i) $\sqrt[3]{a^2} \times \sqrt{a^3} \div a^2$

(j) $12p^{\frac{7}{8}} \div \sqrt{16p^2}$

(k) $\sqrt[3]{27p^6} \times (4p^{-2})^{\frac{1}{2}}$

7. Solve the following equations where $x > 0$.

(a) $x^{\frac{1}{3}} = 4$

(b) $3x^{\frac{1}{4}} = 2$

(c) $x^{-\frac{1}{2}} = 5$

(d) $x^{\frac{3}{2}} = 8$

(e) $x^{-\frac{1}{7}} = 2$

(f) $x^{\frac{1}{20}} = 1$

(g) $x^{-\frac{2}{5}} = \dfrac{1}{9}$

(h) $x^{\frac{2}{3}} = \dfrac{1}{16}$

(i) $(2x)^{\frac{2}{5}} = 100$

(j) $(x-1)^{-\frac{3}{4}} = \dfrac{8}{27}$

(k) $(3x+2)^{-\frac{3}{2}} = \dfrac{1}{64}$

8. Solve the following equations for x and/or y.

(a) $27^x = 3$

(b) $16^x = \dfrac{1}{4}$

(c) $25^{3x+1} = 5$

(d) $4^x = 128$

(e) $\left(\dfrac{1}{9}\right)^x = 243$

(f) $2^{x+2} = 16^{\frac{7}{4}}$

(g) $4^x \cdot 3^{2x} = 6$

(h) $4^{x(x-1)} = 16$

(i) $2^{x+2y} = 8$

(j) $3^x \cdot 9^{2y} = 27$

$\quad\;\; 9^{2x-y} = 3$

$\quad\;\; 2^x \cdot 4^{-y} = \dfrac{1}{8}$

4

9. Given that $a = x^{\frac{m}{n}}$,
   (a) make x the subject of the formula,
   (b) hence, or otherwise, evaluate x when $a = 8$, $m = 6$ and $n = 2$.

Express the following in its simplest form.

10. (a) $4x - (2x + 7)$
    (b) $-4x(2x + 7)$

11. (a) $2x - 3(-2x - 3)$
    (b) $(2x - 3)(-2x - 3)$

12. (a) $4b - 3a - (2a + 5b)$
    (b) $4b - 3a(-2a + 5b)$

13. $3xy(4xy^2 - 5x^2y)$

14. $(1 + 3x)(2 - 6x)$

15. $(5x - 4)(3x^2 + 2x - 1)$

16. $(x^2 - 2x + 4)(x^3 - 2x + 5)$

17. $(2x + 5)(2x - 5) - 2x + 5(2x - 5)$

18. $2(4x - 7)^2$

19. $3(2x - 3y)(3 + 2x - 3y)$

20. $(2x - 3)^2(2x + 3)$

21. $(x + 2)^2(x - 2)^2$

22. $(2x - 1)^2(x + 3)^2$

23. $3(2x + 1) - 4[2x - (x + 5)]$

24. $x(4x - y) - (2x - 3y)^2 - 3y(x - 3y)$

25. $2(4b - 3a) - (-2a + 5b) + 4a - 3b$

26. $2(a + b - c) - 3(b + c - a) + 4(c + a - b)$

27. $-(x - y) + (-x + y) - (-x - y)$

28. $x(y^2 - z^3) - y^2(z^3 + x) - z^3(x - y^2)$

29. $a^2(a + 2) + a(a^2 - 2) - 2(a^2 + a)$

Factorise the following completely.

30. $3x + 12x^3$

31. $4(2 + a) - a^2(2 + a)$

32. $4x^2y^2 - 100$

33. $2u^2 - 50u^4$

34. $13x^2 - 31x - 24$

35. $6y^2 + 3xy - 30x^2$

36. $11x - 6x^2 - 4$

37. $9a - 18b - 3(a - 2b)^2$

38. $3px - 4py + 8xy - 6x^2$

39. $(x - 2y)^2 - 9(2x + y)^2$

40. $2a^3bc - 8a^4b^3c - 24a^5b^5c$

41. $(m^2 + 1)(n - 4) - 2m(4 - n)$

Simplify the following algebraic fractions, giving your answers in the lowest terms.

42. $\dfrac{51m^3np^2}{153mn^2p^3}$

43. $\dfrac{(-2xy)^3}{-6xy^2}$

44. $\dfrac{4xy^2(x + y)}{12x^2y(x + y)}$

45. $\dfrac{6a^2(a - 2b)}{9a^3(a - 2b)^2}$

46. $\dfrac{32a^6 b^4}{6a^2 b \times (4ab)^2}$

47. $\dfrac{10(p^2 q)^3}{(2q)^3 p^5} \div \dfrac{45p}{(6q)^2}$

48. $\dfrac{4x^3 y^4}{7x^4 y^4} \div 2y \times \dfrac{21x}{6y}$

49. $\dfrac{x^2 y^{n+2} z^{2n}}{xy^{n+3} z^n}$

50. $\dfrac{15a^n b^3}{18a^{n-2} b^{n+4}}$

51. $\dfrac{7a^n b^3}{24b^{10} c^{n+3}} \div \dfrac{a^3 c}{18b^7 c^{n+4}}$

Simplify the following, giving your answers in the lowest terms.

52. $\dfrac{3ab + 2a^2}{6a^3}$

53. $\dfrac{2xy + 4x}{y^2 + 2y}$

54. $\dfrac{x^2 + y^2}{x^2 - y^2}$

55. $\dfrac{(m - n)^2}{m^2 - n^2}$

56. $\dfrac{(2m - 2n)^2}{(7m - 7n)^2}$

57. $\dfrac{pq - q^2}{(q - p)^2}$

58. $\dfrac{p^2 + 5p - 6}{p^2 - 36}$

59. $\dfrac{4 - 4u}{u^2 - u}$

60. $\dfrac{a^2 b^3 - 3a^3 b^2}{3a^2 - 10ab + 3b^2}$

61. $\dfrac{c^2 + 7c + 10}{10c - 2c^2}$

62. $\dfrac{x^2 - y^2}{y^2 - xy}$

63. $\dfrac{5a^2 - a(2a + 3)}{4a(a - 1) - 3a + 3}$

Express each of the following as a single fraction in its lowest terms.

64. $\dfrac{2x + 7}{3x - 1} - \dfrac{x + 15}{2(3x - 1)}$

65. $\dfrac{4}{2x + 4} + \dfrac{8}{x^2 - 4}$

66. $\dfrac{3x + 4}{x^2 + 3x + 2} - \dfrac{1}{x + 1}$

67. $\dfrac{6}{x^2 + 3x} - \dfrac{10}{2x^2 + 7x + 3}$

68. $\dfrac{x}{x - 5} + \dfrac{x - 2}{x^2 - 3x - 10}$

69. $\dfrac{1}{x^2 + 2x} - \dfrac{1}{2x}$

70. $\dfrac{4x^2}{9 - x^2} + \dfrac{2x}{x - 3}$

71. $\dfrac{3}{2(m - 1)} - \dfrac{5}{3m} - \dfrac{9}{6m^2 - 6m}$

72. $\dfrac{5}{x + 1} - \dfrac{2}{x + 3} - \dfrac{4}{x^2 + 4x + 3}$

73. $\dfrac{7}{x^2 + 5x - 6} - \dfrac{2}{x^2 + 6x} - \dfrac{1}{x^2 - x}$

74. (a) Simplify $\dfrac{a^2 - b^2}{a^2 + 2ab + b^2}$.

(b) Hence, evaluate $\dfrac{a^2 - b^2}{a^2 + 2ab + b^2}$ when $a = 4.7$ and $b = 3.9$, giving your answer correct to 3 significant figures.

75. Evaluate the following without using a calculator. Give your answer as a fraction in its simplest form.

(a) $\dfrac{a - b}{a^2 - ab}$ if $a = \dfrac{3}{8}$ and $b = \dfrac{5}{7}$

(b) $\dfrac{(a + b)^2}{b^2 - a^2}$ if $a = 55$ and $b = -33$

76. Evaluate $\dfrac{2x^2 - 3x}{2x^2 - x - 3}$ when $x = 1.25$ without the use of a calculator.

77. Simplify $\dfrac{x^2 - 6xy + 9y^2}{x^2 - 3xy}$ and hence, find the value of this expression when $x = \dfrac{1}{3}$

and $y = \dfrac{1}{12}$.

78. Evaluate $a - \dfrac{b^2}{a}$ for each of the following sets of values of a and b. Give your answers correct to 2 decimal places.

(a) $a = 3.6$ and $b = 1.4$

(b) $a = \dfrac{7}{12}$ and $b = \dfrac{5}{12}$

79. Find, without the use of a calculator, the exact value of $\dfrac{a^2 - b^2}{c}$ for each of the following sets of values of a, b and c.

(a) $a = 7.85$, $b = 4.15$ and $c = 1.2$

(b) $a = 8.25$, $b = 2.75$ and $c = 110$

80. Find the exact value of $\dfrac{ac + bc}{ab + a^2}$ if $a = \dfrac{2}{9}$, $b = 1\dfrac{3}{5}$ and $c = \dfrac{4}{3}$.

81. Evaluate $\dfrac{ab + ac}{b^2 - d^2}$ if $a = 5.2$, $b = 5.6$, $c = 4.4$ and $d = 0.4$.

Solve the following equations. If the answer is inexact, give your answers correct to 3 significant figures.

1. $0.817 + \dfrac{x}{0.215} = 0.906$

2. $\dfrac{3}{2}\left(\dfrac{4}{3} - 6x\right) = \dfrac{9}{4}$

3. (a) $27^2 - x^2 = 15^2$
   (b) $-27^2 + x^2 = 15^2$

4. (a) $-3.21 + \sqrt{x} = 1.54$
   (b) $-3.21\sqrt{x} = 1.54$

5. (a) $\sqrt{\dfrac{17}{13}} + \sqrt{x} = \sqrt{\dfrac{15}{13}}$
   (b) $\sqrt{\dfrac{17}{13}} - x = \sqrt{\dfrac{15}{13}}$

6. (a) $(41 - \sqrt{x})^2 = 6.25$
   (b) $\sqrt{41 - x^2} = 6.25$

7. $x - \dfrac{11}{14} = \sqrt{\left(\dfrac{11}{14}\right)^2 - \dfrac{3}{7}}$

8. $\left(x + \dfrac{7}{10}\right)^2 = \dfrac{2}{5} + \left(\dfrac{7}{10}\right)^2$

9. $x - \dfrac{7}{3} = \dfrac{-\sqrt{24 + 14^2}}{6}$

Make x the subject of each of the following:

10. $w = \dfrac{y}{xy - w}$

11. $a = \dfrac{ax - b}{b(a - bx)}$

12. $ax = \dfrac{x}{b} + \dfrac{1}{cx}$

13. $p(x - r)^2 + r = px^2$

14. $x = A\sqrt{\dfrac{x}{Ay}}$

15. $p = T\sqrt{\dfrac{x^2 + p^2}{x^2}}$

16. $x - 1 = \sqrt{\dfrac{p^2x^2 + 1}{p^2}}$

Solve the following equations. Give your answers correct to 3 significant figures where applicable.

17. (a) $2x - 19 = 6(x - 2)$
    (b) $2x^2 - 19 = 6(x - 2)$

18. (a) $2y^2 - 17 = 0$
    (b) $2y^2 = 17y$
    (c) $2y^2 + 17 = 17y$

19. (a) $2x(2x - 3) = 0$
    (b) $2x(2x - 3) = -2$
    (c) $2x(2x - 3) = 3$

20. (a) $(3x - 1)(3x + 1) = 0$
    (b) $(3x - 1)(3x + 1) = 9$
    (c) $(3x - 1)^2 = 9$
    (d) $(3x - 1)(x + 3) = 9$

21. (a) $10y - (21 - y) = 1$
(b) $10 - (21 - y)^2 = 1$
(c) $10y - (21 - y^2) = 1$
(d) $10y - (21 - y)^2 = 1$

22. (a) $1 - 3(2x + 1) = x - 3$
(b) $1 - 3x(2x + 1) = x - 3$
(c) $(1 - 3x)(2x + 1) = x - 3$

Solve the following equations by completing the squares. Give your answers correct to 2 decimal places where applicable.

23. $x^2 + 4x + \dfrac{5}{3} = 0$

24. $4x^2 - 7x + 2 = 0$

25. $3x^2 + \dfrac{8}{3}x - 1 = 0$

26. $x(x - 3) = 13$

27. $3x^2 + 5x + 1 = \dfrac{1}{4}$

Solve the following equations by formula. Give your answers correct to 2 decimal places where applicable.

28. $8x^2 - 17x + 8 = 0$

29. $\dfrac{1}{2}x^2 + \dfrac{4}{3}x + \dfrac{5}{9} = 0$

30. $(x + 1)^2 = 3x(3 - x)$

Solve the following equations. Give your answers correct to 2 decimal places where applicable.

31. $x - \dfrac{2}{3} = \dfrac{1}{4}x^2$

32. $\dfrac{x^2}{2} + \dfrac{1}{3} = \dfrac{x}{3} + 1$

33. $6 + x - \dfrac{9}{x} = 0$

34. $\dfrac{3}{x} - (x + 2) = 5$

35. $\dfrac{3}{2x} + \dfrac{9}{x^2} = 2$

36. $6 - \dfrac{1}{x - 5} = 2x$

37. $x = \dfrac{7}{3} + \dfrac{5}{x}$

38. $\dfrac{x}{3} - \dfrac{5}{x + 2} = 0$

39. $\dfrac{6}{x} + \dfrac{3}{x - 1} = 2$

40. $\dfrac{8}{2x - 3} = \dfrac{4}{x - 1} + 5$

41. $\dfrac{2x + 1}{3 - x} = \dfrac{3 - x}{3x - 1}$

42. $\dfrac{x + 2}{x - 2} = 2x$

43. $\dfrac{1}{x - 5} - \dfrac{8}{x + 1} = \dfrac{1}{3}$

44. A man finds that it takes 14 minutes less to cut his lawn with a new mower which cuts at 10.5 m²/min faster than his old one. The area of his lawn is 432 m².
(a) Taking x to be the rate, in m² per minute, at which the new mower cuts, write down an expression, in terms of x, for the time taken to cut the lawn with
(i) the new mower, (ii) the old mower.
(b) Hence, form an equation in x and show that it reduces to $2x^2 - 21x - 648 = 0$.
(c) Solve this equation and find the time taken to cut the lawn with the new mower.

45. Find x if the area of the shaded ring in the figure below is 17π cm^2. Give your answer correct to 3 significant figures.

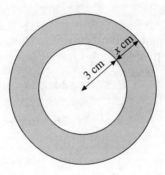

46. If $x = -2$ is a solution to the equation $kx^2 - 8x - 2k^2 = 0$, find the values of k.

47. A square of side y cm and a rectangle of sides $(4y + 1)$ cm and $(y - 2)$ cm both have the same area. Form an equation in y and show that it reduces to $3y^2 - 7y - 2 = 0$. Solve this equation and hence, state, correct to the nearest mm, the perimeter of the square.

48. A dealer bought x vases for $1 400 and proposed to sell them at a profit of $30 per vase.
    (a) Write down, in terms of x, an expression for the selling price of each vase.
    (b) When the dealer had sold all except 200 vases, he found that he had received $2 500. Form an equation in x and show that it reduces to $3x^2 - 170x - 2\ 800 = 0$.
    (c) Solve the equation $3x^2 - 170x - 2\ 800 = 0$ and hence state
        (i) the cost price of each vase,
        (ii) the number of vases he had sold.

49.

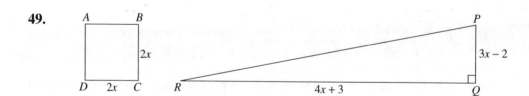

ABCD is a square of side $2x$ cm. PQR is a triangle in which $PQ = (3x - 2)$ cm, $QR = (4x + 3)$ cm and $P\hat{Q}R = 90°$. Given that the area of the square ABCD is equal to the area of the triangle PQR, form an equation in x and show that it reduces to $4x^2 + x - 6 = 0$. Solve this equation and find the area of the square, giving your answers correct to 2 decimal places.

50. A van travelled from town X to town Y, which were 220 km apart, at an average speed of x km/h. A bus travelled by the same route from town X to town Y at an average speed which was 3 km/h faster than the speed of the van.

(a) Given that the difference between the two vehicles in reaching town Y was 12 minutes, write down an equation in x and show that it reduces to $x^2 + 3x - 3\ 300 = 0$.

(b) Solve the equation $x^2 + 3x - 3\ 300 = 0$, giving each of your answers correct to 1 decimal place.

(c) Hence, find, in hours and minutes, the time it took the van to travel from town X to town Y.

51.

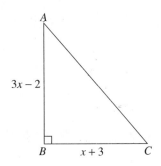

In the diagram, $A\hat{B}C = 90°$, $AB = (3x - 2)$ cm and $BC = (x + 3)$ cm.

(a) If the area of the triangle is 17 cm^2, form an equation in x and solve it.

(b) If, instead, the length of AC is 17 cm, form an equation in x and solve it. Hence, find the perimeter of the triangle, giving your answer correct to 3 significant figures.

52. A cyclist travelled 6 km uphill at an average speed of x km/h and then 9 km downhill at an average speed of $(x + 4.5)$ km/h. Given that the total time taken for the whole journey is 44 minutes, write down an equation in x and show that it reduces to $22x^2 - 351x - 810 = 0$. Solve this equation and hence, find the time in minutes the cyclist took to travel the 9 km journey downhill.

53. Mr Joseph paid $40 for x litres of grade A petrol. He found that if he had bought grade B petrol costing 15 cents less per litre, he could have obtained 5 litres more for the same amount of money.

(a) Write down, in terms of x, an expression for
  (i) the price per litre of grade A petrol,
  (ii) the price per litre of grade B petrol.

(b) Write down an equation which x must satisfy and show that it reduces to $3x^2 + 15x - 4\ 000 = 0$.

(c) Solve this equation and state, correct to 3 significant figures, the number of litres of grade A petrol which can be bought for $40.

(d) Find, correct to 3 decimal places, the price per litre of grade B petrol.

TEST PAPER 1

Time : 1 hour
Marks : 50

1. Evaluate the following:

(a) $8^{-\frac{3}{4}} \times 2^{-\frac{3}{4}}$ [2]

Ans _____

(b) $\dfrac{\left(27^{\frac{1}{3}}\right)^{\frac{5}{2}}}{27^{-\frac{1}{2}}}$ [2]

Ans _____

(c) $\left(\dfrac{1}{2}\right)^{5} \times 4^{1.5} + \left(\dfrac{8}{27}\right)^{-\frac{2}{3}}$ [2]

Ans _____

2. Simplify the following:

(a) $\left(a^{\frac{1}{2}}b^{2}\right)^{\frac{3}{4}} \times \left(ab^{-8}\right)^{\frac{1}{8}}$ [2]

Ans _____

(b) $\sqrt[3]{8p^6} \div \left(16p^{-2}\right)^{\frac{1}{2}}$ [2]

Ans _____

3. Expand and simplify the following: [2]
   (a) $(x + 2y)(x - 2y)^2$

Ans _____

   (b) $a(2b - 3c) - 2b(a - 3c) + 3c(a + 2b)$ [2]

Ans _____

4. Factorise completely:
   (a) $14 + 26x - 4x^2$ [2]

Ans _____

(b) $4 - 4a^2 + a^2b^2 - b^2$ [3]

Ans _____

5. (a) Simplify $\dfrac{a^2 + ab}{a^2 - b^2}$. [2]

(b) Hence, evaluate $\dfrac{a^2 + ab}{a^2 - b^2}$ when $a = \dfrac{2}{3}$ and $b = \dfrac{2}{7}$. [2]

Ans (a) _____

(b) _____

6. Simplify:

(a) $\dfrac{4x^2 - 9}{2x^2 + x - 3} \times \dfrac{x - 1}{2x^2 - 3x}$ [3]

Ans _____

(b) $\dfrac{3}{x(x - 1)} - \dfrac{x + 3}{(x - 1)(x + 2)}$ [3]

Ans _____

7. Make x the subject of each of the following:

(a) $a^2 = \dfrac{ax^2}{b} + c^2$ [2]

Ans _____

(b) $mx + \dfrac{n}{x} = n\sqrt{\dfrac{1}{x^2} + x^2}$ [2]

Ans _____

8. Solve the following equations by formula. Give your answers correct to 2 decimal places where applicable.

(a) $x^2 - \dfrac{9}{4}x - \dfrac{2}{3} = 0$ [2]

Ans _____

(b) $7 - 3x^2 = 2 + x - x^2$ [2]

Ans _____

9. A scooterist travelled a distance of 30 km at an average speed of *x* km/h. If he reduced his speed by 10 km/h, he would take 8 minutes longer for the same journey. Find *x*, giving your answer correct to 1 decimal place. [5]

Ans _____

10. *PQRS* is a trapezium in which *PS* // *QR* and $P\hat{Q}R = 90°$. The lengths of *PQ*, *QR* and *PS* are $(2x - 1)$ cm, $(3x - 8)$ cm and $(5x - 6)$ cm respectively.

(a) Write down, in terms of *x*, an expression for the area of the trapezium. [1]

(b) Given that the area of the trapezium is 31 cm², form an equation in *x* and show that it reduces to $4x^2 - 9x - 12 = 0$. [3]

(c) Solve $4x^2 - 9x - 12 = 0$, giving your answers correct to 2 decimal places. Hence, find the length of *PS*. [4]

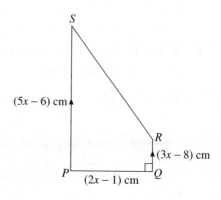

Ans (a) _____

(c) _____

1. Find the range of values of x determined by each of the following inequalities.

    (a) $2x - 9 > 4(3 + 2x)$

    (b) $\frac{1}{2}(3x - 2) \leqslant \frac{2}{3}(x - 9)$

    (c) $\frac{1}{4}(3x + 1) - \frac{1}{6}(x + 1) < \frac{3}{8}(2x - 1)$

    (d) $3x - 2 < 5x + 6 \leqslant 15 - 4x$

    (e) $-\frac{5}{2} < \frac{1 - 3x}{2} < -\frac{2}{5}$

2. List the integer values of k such that

$$\frac{k}{4} < 5\sqrt{3.6} < \frac{k}{4} + 1.$$

3. Find the positive integer x for which

$$280 < \frac{5x^2}{3} < 290.$$

4. List the integer values of y which satisfy each of the following inequalities.

    (a) $-4 \leqslant y + 4 \leqslant 1$ and $12 < \frac{y}{2} + 15$

    (b) $-8 < 4 - 3y < -3$

    (c) $5y - 8 \leqslant 27 < 8y - 5$

    (d) $2 \leqslant 4y - 13 \leqslant \frac{2}{3}(3y - 4)$

5. Given that x is an integer and that

$$-69 < 2x + 1 \leqslant 69,$$

    write down

    (a) the least value of x,

    (b) the greatest value of x such that x is a perfect square,

    (c) two values of x which are exactly divisible by both -11 and 2,

    (d) the difference between the largest and the smallest prime number.

6. Given that $4 - 3x < 2x + 17$ and $5 + 4x \leqslant 9$, write down

    (a) the largest integer value of x,

    (b) the smallest integer value of x,

    (c) the smallest rational value of x.

7. If $\frac{4}{3} \leqslant x \leqslant 5$ and $-7 \leqslant y \leqslant 2$,

   (a) find the largest possible value of
     (i) $y - x$,   (ii) $x^2 + y^2$.
   (b) find the smallest possible value of
     (i) $y^2 - x^2$,   (ii) $x + y$.

8. Given that $2\frac{1}{2} \leqslant x \leqslant 10$ and $0.4 \leqslant y \leqslant 5$, calculate

   (a) the largest possible value of $\frac{x}{y}$,

   (b) the smallest possible value of xy,
   (c) the largest possible value of $2y - x^2$.

9. Given that x and y are integers such that $2 < x < 5$ and $4 < y < 9$, determine

   (a) the maximum value of $\dfrac{x + y}{y - x}$,

   (b) the minimum value of $\dfrac{xy}{y - x}$,

   (c) the minimum value of $\dfrac{y^2}{x}$,

   (d) the maximum value of $(x - y)^2$.

10. Find the three integer values of x which satisfy the inequalities $5x - 8 \leqslant 3x + 8 \leqslant 4x + 2$. Given that p and q are any two of these three values of x, write down the values of p and q which would give

   (a) $\dfrac{1}{p} + \dfrac{1}{q}$ its smallest value,

   (b) $\dfrac{1}{pq}$ its largest value,

   (c) $\dfrac{1}{p} - \dfrac{1}{q}$ its least value,

   (d) $\dfrac{p}{q}$ its greatest value.

11. (a) The mass of a packet of cookies is 200 g, correct to the nearest 10 g. What is the range within which the true mass of the packet of cookies lies?
   (b) A boy's height is recorded as 159 cm, correct to the nearest cm. Between what limits of accuracy may his height lie?
   (c) Find the limits between which the actual volume of a liquid, which is given as 2.34 l, correct to the nearest 0.01 l, lie.
   (d) A cross-country route of 4.8 km, measured to 1 decimal place, is to be covered. Find the limits between which the distance covered by any runner lie.

12. The measurements of a rectangle are given as 4.8 cm and 2.6 cm, correct to 1 decimal place. Find the greatest possible area and the least possible perimeter of the rectangle.

13. (a) A length of 35 cm is cut off a metal rod of length 50 cm. Both measurements are given to the nearest cm. Between what limits may the remaining length lie?

(b) A beaker has 50 cm^3 of water. When some marbles are put into the beaker, the volume becomes 195 cm^3. Find the limits between which the volume of the marbles lie, if the measurements are given correct to the nearest cm^3.

(c) The mass of a truck and its load of cargo is 7.24 tons, correct to the nearest 0.01 tons. Find the minimum and maximum possible mass of the cargo, in kg, if the mass of the empty truck is 3.84 tons, correct to the nearest 0.01 tons.

14. (a) The sides of an isosceles triangle are given as 7 cm, 7 cm and 5 cm, correct to 1 significant figure. Calculate the greatest and least possible perimeter of the triangle.

(b) The sides of the same triangle are given as 7.0 cm, 7.0 cm and 5.0 cm, correct to 2 significant figures. Calculate the greatest and least possible perimeter of the triangle.

15. A rectangular fish tank is exactly 90 cm long, but 50 cm wide and 60 cm high, correct to the nearest cm. If water is filled up to a height of 45 cm (correct to the nearest cm) of the tank, calculate the limits between which the volume of water in the tank may lie. Give your answers correct to the nearest litre.

16. The length of a side of a square is 11 cm, correct to the nearest cm. Find
(a) the largest possible area,
(b) the smallest possible perimeter of the square.

17. A box contains 3 marbles. Each marble has a mass of 200 g, correct to the nearest gram, and a volume of 40 cm^3, correct to the nearest cm^3. The box has a mass of 30 g, correct to the nearest gram. Find the largest possible value of
(a) the mass of a marble,
(b) the density of marble, correct to 3 significant figures,
(c) the total mass of the 3 marbles and the box.

18. The volume of a substance is found by dividing the mass by the density. If the mass of the substance is found to be 4.4 g (correct to the nearest 0.1 g) and its density is 0.9 g/cm^3 (correct to the nearest 0.1 g/cm^3), find
(a) the limits between which the mass lie,
(b) the greatest and least possible volume of the substance, correct to 3 significant figures.

19. The mass and height of 6 children are shown in the table below. All measurements are made correct to the nearest unit shown. Find
   (a) the maximum average mass,
   (b) the minimum average height of the 6 children.

Mass (0.1 kg)	14.5	15.0	13.5	14.0	14.5	15.0
Height (cm)	73	75	75	76	74	75

20. A particle travelled for 7 s at 200 m/s, correct to the nearest second. Calculate the least possible distance travelled by the particle.

21. A reel contains 91.8 m of cotton. 50 pieces of cotton each of length 1.5 m are cut from the reel. If all the measurements are made correct to the nearest 0.1 m, find the limits between which the remaining cotton on the reel must lie.

22. O is the centre of a circle of radius 3 cm, correct to the nearest cm. Given that A and B are two points on the circumference of the circle and that angle AOB measures 70° exactly, calculate
   (a) the maximum possible length of the arc AB,
   (b) the minimum possible area of the sector AOB, expressing each answer as a fraction in its lowest terms.

$$\left(\text{Take } \pi \text{ to be } \frac{22}{7} \right)$$

23. Find the least possible volume of each of the solids, giving your answers correct to the nearest cm³. All measurements are given correct to the nearest cm.

(a)

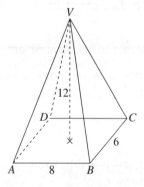

VABCD is a pyramid with a horizontal rectangular base ABCD.

(b)

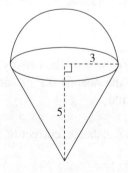

A hemisphere with radius 3 cm joined to a cone of height 5 cm.

24. If the two equal sides of an isosceles triangle are 10 cm each, what is the possible length of the third side?

25. Two sides of a triangle are 8 cm and 6 cm long. If the length of the third side is an integer, how many different triangles can be formed? What are the possible lengths of the third side if the triangle is an isosceles triangle?

26. Use matchsticks as unit length to form a rectangle each time so that the length is at least 5 units but not more than 8 units and the width is less than 3 units. Find the areas of all the rectangles formed.

27. Peter decides to buy some canoes and some paddle-boats for use in his boating lake. He decides to buy at least 4 but less than 7 canoes and not less than 6 paddle-boats. The maximum number of boats he wishes to buy is 12. List all the possible combinations of boats that he can buy.

28. The owner of a large piece of land plans to divide it into not more than 36 plots and to build either a terrace or a bungalow on each plot. He decides that he will build at least 20 terraces and that the number of terraces will be 8 more than the number of bungalows. What is the maximum number of bungalows that he can build?

29. Rahman spent $12 to buy 100 apples. If he sold an apple for 30 cents, what was the least number of apples that he had to sell in order to make a profit of at least $5?

30. Mr Wang has 3 luggage bags to check in at the airport. If 2 of his luggage bags weigh 7 kg and 5.6 kg respectively, what is the maximum mass of the third luggage bag if an average mass of not more than 6 kg is allowed to be checked in?

31. Joe and Ahmad have more than 80 marbles altogether. Ahmad has at least 4 times as many marbles as Joe. What is the least number of marbles each have?

32. The length of a room is 4 m more than its width. If the perimeter is not more than 88 m, what are the possible lengths of the room?

33. If 17 is added to 3 times of x, the result is at least 44. What are the possible values of x? Represent the solution set on a number line.

34. How many sets of 4 consecutive numbers can be obtained if their sum is less than 50?

35. List the set of 3 consecutive even numbers whose sum is not more than 64 and whose smallest even number is at least 12.

36. A positive integer, when multiplied by 6 and has 21 added to it, gives a result greater than when it is multiplied by 8 and has 7 subtracted from it. Find the possible values of x.

37. Half of a number added to 12 is more than one-third of it added to 13.
    (a) What are the possible members of the set?
    (b) What is the smallest possible integer satisfying the set?

38. 7 is subtracted from 3 times a number and the difference is then halved. If the result is less than or equal to 40, what is the greatest integer value of the number?

39. If a number is trebled, the result is less than when 28 is added to it. What are the possible members of the set?

40. Peter has 25 sweets and Lilian has 55. How many sweets must Peter give Lilian in order that Lilian will have more than 4 times of what Peter has?

1. Find **(i)** the midpoint,
   (ii) the length,
   (iii) the gradient of the line segment with the following endpoints.

   (a) $(2, -1)$ and $(6, 2)$ **(b)** $(0, 18)$ and $(5, 6)$

   (c) $(1, -5)$ and $\left(3, -3\frac{1}{2}\right)$ **(d)** $\left(-1\frac{2}{3}, -\frac{8}{9}\right)$ and $\left(-4\frac{1}{3}, \frac{10}{9}\right)$

   (e) $(3, 5)$ and $(5, 3)$ **(f)** $(0, -3)$ and $(-8, 3)$

   (g) $(-2, 5)$ and $(3, 5)$ **(h)** $(4, 7)$ and $(4, 13)$

   (i) $\left(1\frac{1}{2}, 5\right)$ and $\left(4, 9\frac{1}{2}\right)$ **(j)** $(-2, 5)$ and $(-3, 1)$

   (k) (a, b) and (p, q) **(l)** $(2p, p)$ and $(8p, 9p)$

   (m) $(3p^2, 2q)$ and $(6p^2, 5q)$

2. The coordinates of the points A and B are $(3, -8)$ and $(p, 7)$ respectively. Find p if
   (a) the distance between the points A and B is 17 units,
   (b) the gradient of the line joining the points A and B is 10,
   (c) the midpoint of the line segment with endpoints at A and B lies on the y-axis.

3. **(a)** Find the perimeter of the triangle with vertices $A(3, -1)$, $B(-1, 4)$ and $C(-2, -5)$. What type of triangle is triangle ABC?
   (b) Find the perimeter of the quadrilateral with vertices $A(0, 2)$, $B(5, 3)$, $C(7, 6)$ and $D(2, 5)$. Show that $ABCD$ is a parallelogram.

4. The vertices of a rectangle are $A(-2, -2)$, $B(2, 0)$, $C(1, 2)$ and $D(a, b)$. Find
   (a) the point of intersection of the diagonals,
   (b) the coordinates of D,
   (c) the area of rectangle $ABCD$.

5. Given that the distance of $P(0, 3)$ from $A(2a, 0)$ is twice its distance from $B(a, 2a)$, find the possible values of a.

6. **(a)** Find the area of $\triangle ABC$ where $A = (-4, 0)$, $B = (-1, 5)$, $C = (9, -1)$ and $A\hat{B}C = 90°$.
   (b) Find the area of the rhombus $ABCD$ where $A = (0, 4)$, $B = (4, 6)$, $C = (2, 2)$ and $D = (-2, 0)$.

7. The coordinates of the points P, Q and R are $(-1, 11)$, $(2, 5)$ and $(t, 3)$ respectively. Given that $PR = QR$, calculate the value of t. The line PQ is produced to S so that $QS = PQ$. Calculate the coordinates of S.

8. If M is a point on AB such that $AM = MB$, find the value of a and of b in each of the following.
   (a) $A(a, b)$, $B(7, -6)$, $M(4, 2)$
   (b) $A(a, 4)$, $B(b, a)$, $M(2, 3)$
   (c) $A(a, 4)$, $B(7, -6)$, $M(4, b)$

9. By expressing the following equations in the form $y = mx + c$, state the gradient and the y-intercept for each of the following.
   (a) $3y = 4 - 3x$
   (b) $4x - 5y + 7 = 0$

   (c) $\dfrac{x}{4} - \dfrac{y}{6} = 1$
   (d) $x = -\dfrac{1}{4}y - 3$

   (e) $7 - 4x = 2$
   (f) $\dfrac{1 - 6x}{3} = \dfrac{2 - y}{4}$

   (g) $\dfrac{2}{3}x + \dfrac{3}{2}y = 0$
   (h) $\dfrac{2}{3} + \dfrac{3}{2}y = 0$

   (i) $\dfrac{2}{3}x + \dfrac{3}{2} = 0$
   (j) $\dfrac{2}{3}x + \dfrac{3}{2}y = \dfrac{3}{2}$

10.

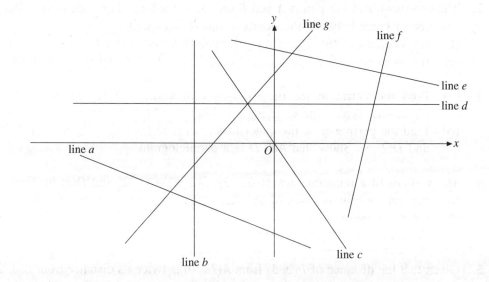

Given $y = mx + c$, write down the line that represents the coordinates given in each case.
   (i) $m > 0$, $c > 0$
   (ii) $m > 0$, $c < 0$
   (iii) $m = 0$, $c > 0$
   (iv) $m < 0$, $c < 0$
   (v) $m < 0$, $c = 0$
   (vi) m is undefined, $c = 0$
   (vii) $m < 0$, $c > 0$

11.

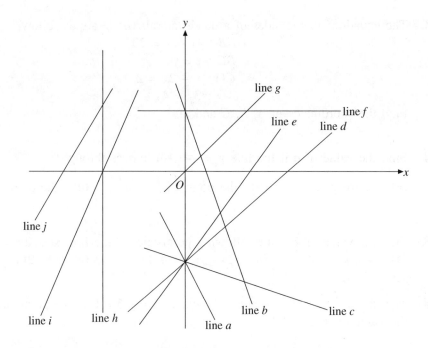

Write down the line that represents each of the following equations.

(i) $x = -4$

(ii) $y = -\frac{1}{2}x - 3$

(iii) $y = -2x - 3$

(iv) $y = 0$

(v) $y = x - 3$

(vi) $y = \frac{2}{3}x$

(vii) $y = \frac{2}{3}x - 3$

(viii) $y - 2 = 0$

(ix) $x = 0$

(x) $y = -2x + 2$

(xi) $y = \frac{4}{3}x + 8$

(xii) $y = \frac{5}{2}x + 10$

12. For each of the following pairs of lines given, calculate
(i) the coordinates of the points of intersection of the lines,
(ii) the distance between the points at which the lines cut the y-axis.

(a) $y = 2x - 5$ and $y = x + 7$

(b) $x - y + 3 = 0$ and the x-axis

(c) $\frac{x}{4} + \frac{y}{5} = 1$ and $y = \frac{5}{4}x + 5$

(d) $x - y = -4$ and $6x - y = 11$

(e) $y = 4x - 3$ and $x = 2$

(f) $3x + 5y = 9$ and $-5x + 2y = 16$

13. The equations of the sides of a quadrilateral $ABCD$ are as follows:
$$AB : 4y + x = 20$$
$$BC : x = 0$$
$$CD : y + 2x = 2$$
$$AD : 3y = 4x - 4$$
Find the coordinates of A, B, C and D.

14. Find the value of c if the line $y = -4x + c$ passes through
   (a) the origin,   (b) the point $\left(2\frac{1}{2}, -3\frac{1}{2}\right)$,   (c) the point $\left(-\frac{2}{3}, 4\frac{1}{3}\right)$.

15. Find the value of k if the following points lie on the line $3x - 2y = 7$.
   (a) $(-5, k)$ (b) $(2k - 1, 2k + 1)$ (c) $(k^2, 2k)$

16. The line $6x + y + 9 = 0$ meets another line $y + 5 = 0$ at the point (a, b). What is the value of a and of b?

17. A straight line passes through the points $(-1, -5)$ and $(3, 7)$. Find
   (a) the coordinates of the points where the line cuts the axes,
   (b) the area of the triangle bounded by the axes and the line.

18. Find the value of m and of c if the line $y = mx + c$ passes through the points
   (a) $(-2, 3)$ and $\left(3, \frac{1}{2}\right)$,   (b) $(0, 4)$ and $(4, 0)$.

19. Find the equation of the line
   (a) with gradient $\frac{1}{2}$ and y-intercept $-\frac{2}{3}$,
   (b) with gradient $-\frac{3}{2}$ and which passes through the point
      (i) $(0, -1)$,   (ii) $(3, 7)$.
   (c) which passes through the point $(4, 8)$ and cuts the y-axis where $y = 2$,
   (d) which is parallel to the line $4x - y = 1$ and which passes through
      (i) the origin,   (ii) the point $(2, 5)$.
   (e) which passes through the points
      (i) $(-4, 7)$ and $(0, 5)$,   (ii) $(4, -7)$ and $(-2, -7)$,
      (iii) $\left(2\frac{1}{2}, -1\right)$ and $\left(2\frac{1}{2}, -6\frac{1}{4}\right)$,   (iv) $(-5, 0)$ and $(0, 7)$,
      (v) $\left(-2, \frac{5}{2}\right)$ and $\left(5, -6\frac{1}{4}\right)$.
   Draw the graph of the line in each of the above cases.

20. The line $2x + 2y = 9$ cuts the x-axis at A and the y-axis at B.
    (a) Find the coordinates of A and B.
    (b) Find the perimeter of $\triangle OAB$, where O is the origin.
    (c) Does the triangle OAB have line symmetry? If it does, find the equation of the line of symmetry.

21. $ABCD$ is a trapezium in which AB is parallel to CD. The vertices A, B, C and D are $(1, 8)$, $(6, 3)$, $(t, -4)$ and $(-6, 5)$ respectively.
    (a) Calculate the value of t.
    (b) Find the length of AD and of BC.
    (c) What type of trapezium is $ABCD$?
    (d) Does the trapezium have line symmetry? If it does, find the equation of the line of symmetry.
    (e) Find the area of the trapezium.
    (f) The diagonals of the trapezium intersect at a point P. Find the coordinates of the point P.

22. Find the gradients of the straight lines AB and PQ in each of the following. Hence deduce if the lines are parallel to each other.
    (a) $A(7, 2)$, $B(8, 5)$; $P(-1, 13)$, $Q(0, 10)$
    (b) $A(9, 1)$, $B(-7, 5)$; $P(-5, -2)$, $Q(-13, 0)$

23. In each of the following, find the equation of the straight line parallel to the given line and passing through the given point.
    (a) $x - 3y + 1 = 0$; $(0, 3)$
    (b) $y = -\dfrac{3}{4}x + 2$; $(1, 8)$
    (c) $\dfrac{x}{3} + \dfrac{y}{2} = 1$; $(4, -1)$

24. Determine if the following pairs of lines intersect each other. If they do, find the point of intersection. If they do not, give a reason to support your answer.
    (a) $y + 1 = \dfrac{3}{4}x$ and $3x - 4y + 11 = 0$
    (b) $y = -\dfrac{3}{2}x - \dfrac{1}{2}$ and $4x + 3y = 15$
    (c) $ax + by = 0$ and $\dfrac{x}{b} + \dfrac{y}{a} + \dfrac{1}{ab} = 0$
    (d) $ax + by = 0$ and $y = -\dfrac{b}{a}x + c$
    (e) $ax + by = 0$ and $y = \dfrac{a}{b}x + c$

25. The diagram shows the graph of a straight line.

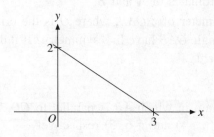

Find **(a)** the equation of the line,
   (b) the equation of the line parallel to the given line and passing through the point $(0, -2)$.

26. Find the value of c if the line $y = 2x + c$ passes through
   (a) the origin,
   (b) the point $(-2, -1)$,
   (c) the point $(3, 0)$.

27. Find the value of k if the following points lie on the line $2x + 3y = 6$.
   (a) $(5, k)$
   (b) $(k, -2)$
   (c) $(2k + 1, 0)$
   (d) $(-1, 1 - 2k)$

28. The line $y + 2x = 8$ meets another line $y = 10$ at the point (a, b). What is the value of a and of b?

29. The line $3x - y = 5$ cuts the x-axis at A and the y-axis at B. Find
   (a) the coordinates of A,
   (b) the coordinates of B.

30. Find the value of m and of c if the line $y = mx + c$ passes through
   (a) $(1, -1)$ and $(2, 1)$,
   (b) $(-1, 4)$ and $(6, -1)$.

Time : 1 hour
Marks : 50

1. (a) Solve the inequality $\frac{5}{3} - x > \frac{3}{4}(2x + 5)$. [2]

Ans _____

(b) List the integer values of y for which $4y \leqslant 13 < 22 + 3y$. [2]

Ans _____

2. Solve the following equations. Give your answers correct to 2 decimal places.
   (a) $3x(x - 5) = 2(2x - 3)$ [3]

Ans _____

(b) $\dfrac{15}{x-2} = 3x - 2, x \neq 2$ [3]

Ans _____

3. It is given that $5 \leqslant a \leqslant 12$ and $-7 \leqslant b < 1$. Find
   (a) the greatest possible value of $a - b$,
   (b) the smallest possible value of $a^2 + b^2$. [2]

Ans (a) _____

(b) _____

4. **(a)** An object travelled 24 m, correct to the nearest m, at a speed of 3 m/s, correct to the nearest m/s. Calculate the greatest possible time taken by the object to cover this distance. [2]

Ans _____

(b) 220 m*l*, 120 m*l* and 50 m*l* of water are poured into 3 cups from a jug containing 900 m*l* of water. If all the measurements are made correct to the nearest 10 m*l*, find the limits between which the volume of water left in the jug must lie. [4]

Ans _____

---

5. Mrs Mok decided to spend \$36 on gifts. She found that a photo frame and an album together cost \$7. If she spent all her money on albums alone, she could buy 3 more gifts than she could if she spent all the money on photo-frames.

(a) Taking the cost of a photo frame to be \$$x$, write down expressions in terms of x for

(i) the cost of an album, [1]

Ans _____

(ii) the number of albums which could be bought for \$36. [1]

Ans _____

(b) Form an equation in x and show that it reduces to $x^2 + 17x - 84 = 0$. Solve this equation and state the cost of a photo frame. [5]

Ans _____

_____

6. Given the points $A(5, 7)$, $B(2, x)$, $C(y, 1)$ and $D(m, n)$,
   (a) find **(i)** the value of x and of y if B is a point on AC such that $AB = BC$,
   [2]

   (ii) the equation of the line through B and cutting AD at the point $(4, -1)$. [3]

   (b) express m in terms of n if the gradient of AD is $\dfrac{2}{3}$. [3]

Ans (a) *(i)* $x =$ _____ , $y =$ _____

(ii) _____

(b) _____

7. (a) Find the coordinates of the points *A*, *B* and *C.*   [4]

(b) Calculate the area of quadrilateral *OABC.* [3]

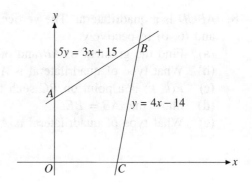

Ans (a)   *A*(,   )

           B(,   )

           C(,   )

(b) _____ sq. units

8. *ABCD* is a quadrilateral. The vertices of *A, B, C* and *D* are (1, 5), (–3, 3), (0, –3) and (6, 0) respectively.
   (a) Find the gradient of *AB* and of *CD*. [2]
   (b) What type of quadrilateral is *ABCD*? [1]
   (c) *E(k, k)* is a point on *BC* such that *AD = DE*. Find the coordinates of *E*. [4]
   (d) Show that *AB = BE*. [2]
   (e) What type of quadrilateral is *ABED*? [1]

Ans (a) gradient of *AB* = _____

gradient of *CD* = _____

(b) _____

(c) E(___ , ___)

(e) _____

CHAPTER 5

Functions and Variations

1. If $f(x) = 5 - (x - 1)^2$, find

   (a) $f\left(\dfrac{1}{4}\right)$,

   (b) x if $f(x) = -4$.

2. If $g(x) = \dfrac{2x + 1}{x - 4}$, find

   (a) $g(0.4)$,

   (b) $g(-5)$,

   (c) $g\left(-\dfrac{3}{2}\right)$.

3. If $h(x) = 3 + \sqrt{x + 1}$, find

   (a) $h\left(\dfrac{9}{16}\right)$,

   (b) x if $h(x) = -2$.

4. Given $f : x \rightarrow \dfrac{3x}{2x - 3}$, find x if

   (a) $f : x \rightarrow \dfrac{3}{4}$,

   (b) $f : x \rightarrow x$.

5. Given $f(x) = 6x + \dfrac{2}{x}$, find x if

   (a) $f(x) = 7$,

   (b) $f(x) = -12$.

6. The function $f : x \rightarrow \dfrac{a}{x} + b$, $(x \neq 0)$, is such that $f(-1) = -4$ and $f(2) = \dfrac{1}{2}$. Find the value of a and of b.

7. Given $h(x) = 4^x$, find

   (a) $h\left(\dfrac{3}{2}\right)$,

   (b) x if $h(x) = \dfrac{1}{64}$.

8. The function f is defined by $f : x \rightarrow \dfrac{x}{x^2 - 1}$, $x \neq \pm 1$. Find

   (a) m if $f : \dfrac{5}{4} \rightarrow m$,

   (b) n if $f : n \rightarrow \dfrac{2}{3}$.

9. The lists below show the relationship between x and y.
   Find, by inspection, an expression $f(x)$ such that $y = f(x)$.

   (a) $x : 1, 2, 3, 4, 5, \ldots$
   $y : 4, 8, 12, 16, 20, \ldots$

   (b) $x : 1, 2, 3, 4, 5, \ldots$
   $y : 3, 5, 7, 9, 11, \ldots$

   (c) $x : 1, 2, 3, 4, 5, \ldots$
   $y : -3, -1, 1, 3, 5, \ldots$

   (d) $x : 1, 2, 3, 4, 5, \ldots$
   $y : 0, 3, 8, 15, 24, \ldots$

   (e) $x : 1, 2, 3, 4, 5, \ldots$
   $y : 2, 4, 8, 16, 32, \ldots$

   (f) $x : 1, 2, 3, 4, 5, \ldots$
   $y : 9.6, 9.2, 8.8, 8.4, 8, \ldots$

10. A function g is defined by $g : x \rightarrow \dfrac{1 - x}{x - 3}$, $x \neq 3$. Find

    (a) $g\left(\dfrac{1}{3}\right)$,   **(b)** $g^{-1}(3)$,   **(c)** $g^{-1}(x)$.

11. Given the function $f : x \rightarrow 6x - \dfrac{20}{x}$, $x \neq 0$. Find

    (a) $f^{-1}(19)$,
    (b) the value of x for which $f^{-1}(x) = -2$.

12. The functions f, g and h are defined by
$$f : x \rightarrow 9 - 2x,$$
$$g : x \rightarrow \dfrac{4}{x - 5}, \ x \neq 5,$$
$$h : x \rightarrow \dfrac{3x + 1}{2x}, \ x \neq 0.$$

    Find **(a)** f^{-1},
           (b) g^{-1},
           (c) h^{-1}.

13. The function f is denoted by $f(x) = \dfrac{1}{4x - 1}$, $x \neq \dfrac{1}{4}$.

    Find $f^{-1}(x)$ and hence find the value of $f^{-1}\left(\dfrac{1}{2}\right)$.

14. The function g is such that $g(x) = 3 + \sqrt{x - 4}$, $x \geq 4$. Find
    (a) $g^{-1}(x)$,   **(b)** $g^{-1}(-1)$.

15. The function f is denoted by $f(x) = x^2 - 4x + 2$. Find

    (a) $f\left(\dfrac{5}{2}\right)$,

    (b) $f^{-1}(-1)$,
    (c) the value of x such that $f^{-1}(x) = 2$,
    (d) the values of x for which $f(x) = 2x$.

16. The function $f(x) = 3x + a$ is such that $f^{-1}(2) = 3$. Find the value of a and of $f^{-1}(-2)$.

17. The function $g(x) = ax + b$ is such that $g^{-1}(4) = 2$ and $g(-3) = 14$. Find the value of a and of b.

18. A function y is given by $g(x) = ax^2 + b$. Find a and b if $g^{-1}(x) = \sqrt{2x - 4}$.

19. A function is denoted by $f(x) = \dfrac{2}{3}(x + 1)$. Find the value of x for which $f(x) = f^{-1}(x)$.

20. The inverse of f is defined by $f^{-1} : x \rightarrow 3 + \dfrac{2}{x}$, $x \neq 0$. Find the rule which defines f.

21. A function f is defined by $f : x \rightarrow \dfrac{x}{2 - x}$, $x \neq 2$. Find f^{-1} and hence, find the values of x for which $f = f^{-1}$.

22. Write down the rule for each of the following variations, expressing y in terms of x and k, where k is a constant.
    (a) y varies directly as the square root of x.
    (b) y is inversely proportional to the cube of x.
    (c) y varies as the reciprocal of x.

23. Describe in words the rule connecting x and y in the following statements:
    (a) $y = kx^2$, where k is a constant
    (b) $y = \dfrac{k}{x + 3}$, where k is a constant

24. Given that p is directly proportional to q^2 and that $p = 27$ when $q = 3$, find
    (a) the rule connecting p and q,
    (b) the value of p when $q = -2$,
    (c) the positive value of q when $p = 48$.

25. Given that y varies as the cube root of x and that $y = 2$ when $x = 27$,
    (a) express y in terms of x,
    (b) calculate the value of x when $y = \dfrac{8}{9}$.

26. Given that y varies inversely as the square of x and that $y = 8$ when $x = 3$, find
    (a) y in terms of x,
    (b) the value of y when $x = -\dfrac{1}{2}$,
    (c) the values of x when $y = 3$.

27. Given that p is inversely proportional to $(q - 2)^2$ and that $p = 4$ when $q = 5$, express p in terms of q. Find the values of q when $p = \dfrac{1}{4}$.

28. The variables x and y are connected by the equation $\dfrac{y}{3 - x} = $ constant. Pairs of corresponding values of x and y are given in the table below.

x	$\dfrac{1}{2}$	7	n
y	5	m	6

Find the value of m and of n.

29. Given that y varies inversely as $\sqrt{2x-1}$ and that $y = 10$ when $x = \dfrac{5}{8}$,

    (a)   write down the law connecting x and y,

    (b)   find the value of y when $x = 13$,

    (c)   find the value of x when $y = -\dfrac{1}{3}$.

30. Given that $xy^2 = k$, where k is a constant and that $x = 8$ when $y = 3$, calculate

    (a)   the value of k,

    (b)   the positive value of y when $x = 4$.

31. Given that y is directly proportional to x^3 and the difference in the values of y when $x = 1$ and when $x = 3$ is 13, find the value of y when $x = -2$.

32. Given that $y \propto px^3 + 2$, find p if $y = 3$ when $x = -1$ and $y = -12$ when $x = 2$. Find the value of x when $y = 3$.

33. Given that $y \propto \dfrac{1}{\sqrt{3x+p}}$, find p if $y = 2$ when $x = 2$ and $y = 3$ when $x = \dfrac{1}{3}$. Hence,

express y in terms of x and find the value of y when $x = 26$.

34. A load of m kg which can be safely carried by a certain kind of chain, whose links have a thickness of t cm, varies directly as the square of t. It is known that when $t = 3$, $m = 4\ 500$.

    (a)   Find the rule connecting m and t.

    (b)   What must be the minimum thickness of the links to withstand a load of 6 480 kg?

    (c)   What is the mass of the load which can be safely carried by a chain whose links have a thickness of 2.5 cm?

35. The volume of a certain object varies as the cube of its diameter. If the volume, V, is 960 mm^3 when the diameter, d, is 4 mm, find

    (a)   the volume, in cm^3, when its diameter is 4.8 cm,

    (b)   the radius when its volume is 405 mm^3.

36. The pressure of water, P, at any point below the surface of the sea varies as the depth of the point below the surface, d.

    (a)   Write an equation connecting P and d using k as the constant.

    (b)   If the pressure is 200 N/m^2 at a depth of 2.5 m, calculate the pressure at a depth of 6 m.

37. Given that y varies as x^n, write down the value of n in each of the following cases.

    (a) y is the surface area of a sphere of radius x.

    (b) y is the volume of a cone of given base area and height x.

    (c) y and x are the base and the corresponding height of a triangle of given area respectively.

38. Given the tables of values of x and y, write down a formula expressing y in terms of x for each of the following tables.

(a)

x	0	1	2	3
y	0	4	32	108

(b)

x	1	4	9
y	5	10	15

(c)

x	1	2	3
y	3	$\dfrac{3}{4}$	$\dfrac{1}{3}$

39. The distance, d, through which a stone falls from rest is proportional to the square of the time, t, taken. If the difference in the values of d when $t = 0$ and $t = 2$ is 28, find the value of d when $t = 2.5$.

40. The number of men needed to dig a trench varies inversely as the time taken to finish it. If 10 men can dig a trench in 4 hours, how long does it take 16 men to dig the same trench. Assume that the men work at the same rate.

41. The speed of an aircraft is inversely proportional to the time taken to complete a journey. If the aircraft takes 15 hours to complete the journey at a speed of 770 km/h, find the time taken for the same journey if its average speed is 825 km/h.

42. The number of pages, N, in a book varies inversely as the number of lines, L, in a page. Given that $N = 400$ when $L = 22$, find L when $N = 550$. How many pages will the book have if there are 32 lines in each page?

43. The radius of a cylinder varies inversely as the square root of its height if the volume of the cylinder is constant. Given that its radius is 9 cm when the height is 16 cm, find
(a) the height when the radius is 3.6 cm,
(b) the radius when the height is 20 cm, giving your answer correct to 1 decimal place.

1. Draw the graphs of each of the following functions.

   (a) $f(x) = \dfrac{10}{x}, -4 \leqslant x \leqslant 4$.

   (b) $g(x) = \dfrac{2}{3}(x - 5), -1 \leqslant x \leqslant 8$.

   (c) $h(x) = 2x^3 - 1, -2 \leqslant x \leqslant 2$. Hence, use your graph to estimate the value of $h(1.7)$.

   (d) $p : x \rightarrow 4^x - 10, -\dfrac{1}{2} \leqslant x \leqslant 2\dfrac{1}{2}$. Hence, estimate from your graph the value of x for which $p(x) = 3$.

   (e) $q : x \rightarrow 2 + x - \dfrac{x^2}{2}, -4 \leqslant x \leqslant 4$. From your graph, estimate the values of x such that $q : x \rightarrow 2x$.

2. (a) Copy and complete the table for $y = 2x^2 - x - 6$.

x	-3	-2	-1	0	1	2	3
y	15	4			-5		9

   (b) Using 2 cm to 1 unit on the x-axis and 1 cm to 1 unit on the y-axis, draw the graph of $y = 2x^2 - x - 6$ for $-3 \leqslant x \leqslant 3$.

   (c) Use your graph to estimate
       (i) the value of y when $x = -0.6$.
       (ii) the values of x when $y = 5$. Hence, write down, but do not simplify, an equation in x which is satisfied by these values of x.
       (iii) the least value of y and the corresponding value of x.

   (d) On the same axes, draw the graph of $y = x + 2$.
       Use your graphs to solve the equation $x^2 - x - 4 = 0$.

3. (a) Given that $y = 2 - x - x^2$, copy and complete the following table.

x	-4	-3	-2	-1	0	1	2	3
y	-10			2	2		-4	-10

   (b) Draw the graph of $y = 2 - x - x^2$, using a scale of 2 cm to 1 unit and 1 cm to 1 unit on the x- and y-axes respectively.

   (c) Draw on your graph the line of symmetry of the curve and write down its equation.

(d) Use your graph to find the range of values of

   (i) y for which $-\dfrac{1}{2} \leqslant x \leqslant \dfrac{1}{2}$,

   (ii) x for which $y < 1$.

(e) By drawing suitable straight-line graphs on the same axes, solve the equations

   (i) $x^2 + x - 5 = 0$,

   (ii) $4 - 2x - x^2 = 0$.

4. The variables x and y are connected by the equation

$$y = x^3 - 9x.$$

   Some corresponding values of x and y are given in the table below.

x	-3	$-2\dfrac{1}{2}$	-2	-1	$-\dfrac{1}{2}$	0	$\dfrac{1}{2}$	1	2	$2\dfrac{1}{2}$	3
y	a	6.9	10	8	4.4	0	b	-8	-10	c	0

   (a) Calculate the values of a, b and c.

   (b) Taking 2 cm to represent 1 unit on each axis, draw the graph of $y = x^3 - 9x$ from $x = -3$ to $x = 3$.

   (c) Describe completely the symmetry of the curve drawn.

   (d) Use your graph to estimate the solutions of the equation $x^3 - 9x - 6 = 0$.

   (e) By drawing a suitable straight line on the same axes, use your graphs to solve the equation $x^3 - 8x = 0$.

   (f) Estimate, from your graph, the gradient of the curve at the point where $x = 0.8$.

5. The following is an incomplete table of values for the function $y = \dfrac{x}{2} - \dfrac{9}{x}$.

x	2	3	4	5	6	7	8	9	10
y	-3.5	-1.5		0.7	1.5		2.9	3.5	

   (a) Calculate and write down the missing values of y.

   (b) Using a scale of 2 cm to 1 unit on each axis, draw the graph of $y = \dfrac{x}{2} - \dfrac{9}{x}$.

   (c) State the range of values of x for which $\dfrac{x}{2} > \dfrac{9}{x}$.

   (d) Estimate the area between the graph $y = \dfrac{x}{2} - \dfrac{9}{x}$, the x-axis and the lines $x = 5.5$ and $x = 8$.

   (e) By drawing a tangent, find the gradient of the graph $y = \dfrac{x}{2} - \dfrac{9}{x}$ at the point $(6, 1.5)$.

6.

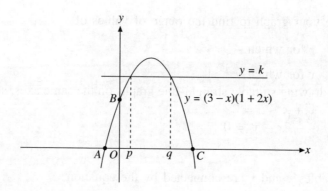

The curve $y = (3 - x)(1 + 2x)$ cuts the x-axis at the points A and C and the y-axis at B.

The line $y = k$ intersects the curve $y = (3 - x)(1 + 2x)$ at the points where $x = p$ and $x = q$.

(a) Write down the coordinates of the points A, B and C.

(b) Find the equation of the line of symmetry of the curve.

(c) Express, in terms of p and q, the range of values of x for which $(3 - x)(1 + 2x) \geqslant k$.

7. (a) Copy and complete the table of values for the function $f(x) = x^2 - 6x + 6$ for $0 \leqslant x \leqslant 6$.

x	0	1	2	3	4	5	6
$f(x)$		1		-3		1	6

(b) Using 2 cm to 1 unit on both axes, draw the graph of $f(x)$.

(c) Describe completely the symmetry of the curve drawn.

(d) Estimate the solutions of the equation
$$x^2 - 6x + 6 = 0.$$

(e) Find, by drawing a suitable straight line on the same axes, the range of values of x for which $x^2 - 6x + 6 < \frac{1}{5}x + 1$.

(f) By drawing the tangent at the point $(5, 1)$, estimate the gradient of the curve at this point.

8. The variables x and y are connected by the equation $y = 4x^2 - 13x - 3$.
Some corresponding values of x and y are given in the table.

x	-1	0	1	2	3	4
y	14	-3	a	-13	b	9

(a) Calculate the value of a and of b.

(b) Taking 2 cm to 1 unit on the x-axis and 1 cm to 1 unit on the y-axis, draw the graph of
$$y = 4x^2 - 13x - 3 \text{ for the range } -1 \leqslant x \leqslant 4.$$

(c) Estimate the solutions of the equation
   (i) $4x^2 - 13x - 3 = 0$,
   (ii) $4x^2 - 13x = 7$.

(d) By drawing a tangent, find the gradient of the curve $y = 4x^2 - 13x - 3$ at the point where $x = 3$.

(e) Estimate the area between the graph $y = 4x^2 - 13x - 3$, the x-axis and the lines $x = 0$ and $x = 2$.

(f) By drawing the line $y = 4x - 9$ on the same axes, find the range of values of x for which $x > 1$ and $4x - 9 < 4x^2 - 13x - 3$.

9. The curve $y = ax^3 + bx + c$ passes through the points $(-1, 0)$, $(0, -2)$ and $(2, 3)$. Find the values of a, b and c.

10. The following is an incomplete table of values for the graph of $y = \dfrac{3}{x^2} + 2$.

x	1.0	1.2	1.4	1.6	1.8	2.0	2.2	2.4
y	5	4.1	3.5	3.2		2.8	2.6	2.5

(a) Calculate and write down the missing value of y.

(b) Taking 1 cm to represent 0.2 unit on the x-axis and 2 cm to represent 1 unit on the y-axis, draw the graph of $y = \dfrac{3}{x^2} + 2$ for values of x from 1.0 to 2.4 inclusive.

(c) Use your graph to solve the equation

$$\frac{3}{x^2} = 1.$$

(d) Using the same axes, draw the graph of $y = x + 3$ and use it to solve the equation

$$\frac{3}{x^2} + 1 = x + 2.$$

(e) State the range of values of x for which $x > 0$ and $\dfrac{3}{x^2} > 2.4$.

11. The following is an incomplete table of values for the function $y = x^2 + x - 2$. Copy and complete the table of values for $-4 \leqslant x \leqslant 3$.

(a)

x	-4	-3	-2	-1	0	1	2	3
y	10	4			-2	0		10

(b) Plot the graph of $y = x^2 + x - 2$ using a scale of 2 cm to 1 unit on the x-axis and 1 cm to 1 unit on the y-axis.

(c) Use your graph to estimate
    (i)   the value of y when $x = -2.5$,
    (ii)   the two values of x which satisfy the equation $x^2 + x - 2 = 3$,
    (iii) the value of x where the function $y = x^2 + x - 2$ has a minimum value,
    (iv) the minimum value of $y = x^2 + x - 2$.

(d) Draw on your graph the line with equation $y = x + 4$. Find the points of intersection of this line and the curve $y = x^2 + x - 2$.

(e) Draw on your graph the line of symmetry of the curve and write down its equation.

12. The variables x and y are connected by the equation $y = 2x^2 - 5x$. Some corresponding values of x and y are given in the following table.

x	−2	−1	0	1	2	3	4
y	a	7	0	−3	b	3	c

(a) Calculate the values of a, b and c.

(b) Taking 2 cm to represent 1 unit on the x-axis and 1 cm to represent 1 unit on the y-axis, draw the graph of $y = 2x^2 - 5x$ for values of x in the range $-2 \leqslant x \leqslant 4$.

(c) Use your graph to find
    (i)   the x-coordinates of the points where $y = 4$,
    (ii)   the coordinates of the minimum point of the curve,
    (iii) the values of x where the curve cuts the x-axis,
    (iv) the values of x where the curve cuts the line $y = -1$,
    (v)   the value of y where the curve cuts the line $x = 1.5$.

(d) On the same axes, draw the graph of the straight line $y = \frac{2}{3}x - 2$ and use your

graphs to solve the equation $2x^2 - 5x = \frac{2}{3}x - 2$.

1. The lists below show the relationship between x and y.
   Find, by inspection, an expression $f(x)$ such that $y = f(x)$.

   (a) $x : 1, 2, 3, 4, 5, \ldots$

   $\quad\quad y : \dfrac{1}{4}, \dfrac{1}{2}, \dfrac{3}{4}, 1, \dfrac{5}{4}, \ldots$ [1]

   (b) $x : 1, 2, 3, 4, 5, \ldots$

   $\quad\quad y : 1, 8, 27, 64, 125, \ldots$ [1]

   Ans (a) _____

   (b) _____

2. Given that $f(x) = x(2x - 1) + 7$, find

   (a) $f(-1)$,

   (b) $f\left(\dfrac{1}{2}\right)$,

   (c) $f^{-1}(8)$. [5]

   Ans (a) _____

   (b) _____

   (c) _____

3. A function g is denoted by

$$g(x) = \frac{4}{3x + 7}, \quad x \neq -\frac{7}{3}.$$

Find **(a)** x if $g : x \to 2$,
     (b) $g^{-1}(x)$,

     (c) $g^{-1}\left(\frac{1}{2}\right)$,

     (d) x if $g^{-1}(x) = 1$.   [8]

Ans (a) _____

    (b) _____

    (c) _____

    (d) _____

4. If $h(x) = ax^2 - 4x + b$, $h(1) = -8$ and $h(-2) = 13$, find the value of a and of b. Hence, evaluate $h(-1)$.   [5]

Ans a = _____

b = _____

h(-1) = _____

5. For a given height, the volume of an object varies directly as the square of its base radius. When the base radius is 2.5 cm, the volume of the object is 10 cm³. Find
   (a) its volume when the base radius is 15 cm,
   (b) its base radius when its volume is 62.5 cm³. [5]

Ans (a) _____

   (b) _____

Answer questions 6 to 8 on graph paper.

6. It is given that $y = 1 + \dfrac{20}{x}$.
   (a) Copy and complete the following table.

x	1	2	3	4	5	6	7	8	9	10
y	21		7.7	6	5	4.3	3.9		3.2	3

[1]

   (b) Taking 1 cm to represent 1 unit on both axes, draw the graph of $y = 1 + \dfrac{20}{x}$ for $1 \leqslant x \leqslant 10$. [3]

   (c) Use your graph to find the range of values of x for which $3 < 1 + \dfrac{20}{x} < 7$. [1]

   (d) By drawing a tangent, find the gradient of the curve $y = 1 + \dfrac{20}{x}$ at the point where $x = 4$. [2]

   (e) By drawing a suitable straight line, use your graph to estimate the solutions of the equation
$$x + \frac{20}{x} - 10 = 0.$$
[2]

7. The variables x and y are connected by the equation
$$y = 5^x.$$

Some corresponding values of x and y (correct to one decimal place where necessary) are given in the table.

x	0	0.2	0.4	0.6	0.8	1.0	1.2	1.4
y	p	1.4	1.9	2.6	q	5	6.9	9.5

(a) Calculate the value of p and of q. [1]
(b) Taking 1 cm to 0.1 unit on the x-axis and 2 cm to 1 unit on the y-axis, draw the graph of $y = 5^x$ for values of x in the range $0 \leqslant x \leqslant 1.4$. [3]
(c) Using your graph, estimate
    (i)   the value of $5^{0.7}$, [1]
    (ii) the solution to the equation $5^x = 3$, [1]
    (iii) the area, in square units, between the graph, the x-axis and the lines $x = 0.5$ and $x = 1$. [2]

8. The variables x and y are connected by the equation
$$y = x^2(2x - 5).$$

Some corresponding values of x and y are given in the table.

x	-1	$-\dfrac{1}{2}$	0	$\dfrac{1}{2}$	1	$1\dfrac{1}{2}$	2	$2\dfrac{1}{2}$	3
y	-7	$-1\dfrac{1}{2}$	0	-1	-3	$-4\dfrac{1}{2}$	-4	0	9

(a) Taking 2 cm to 1 unit on the x-axis and 1 cm to 1 unit on the y-axis, draw the graph of $y = x^2(2x - 5)$, for the range $-1 \leqslant x \leqslant 3$. [3]
(b) From your graph, write down the range of values of x for which
    (i)   the gradient of the curve is negative, [1]
    (ii) $2x^3 - 5x^2 + 2 > 0$. [2]
(c) Draw the line $x - y = 4$ on your diagram.
    Hence, write down the three possible solutions to the equation
$$x^2(2x - 5) = x - 4.$$ [2]

48

1. Find the bearing of *A* from *B* in each of the following.

    (a)

    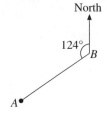

    (b)

    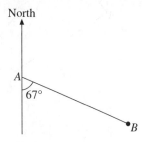

2. Find the bearings of the following.
    (a)   *A*, *B*, *C* and *D* from *O*
    (b)   *O* from *A*, *B*, *C* and *D*

    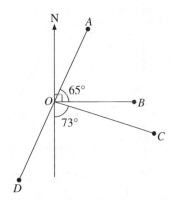

3. In the diagram, *AD* = *BD* = *BC* and *CB̂D* = 94°.
    What are the bearings of
    (a)   *A* from *B*,
    (b)   *B* from *D*,
    (c)   *C* from *B*?

    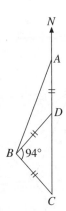

4.

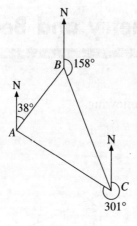

Calculate the bearing of
(a) A from B,
(b) B from C,
(c) C from A.

5.

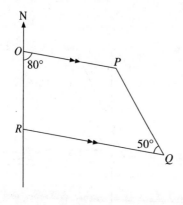

Find (a) the bearing of O from P,
(b) the bearing of P from Q,
(c) the bearing of Q from R.

6.

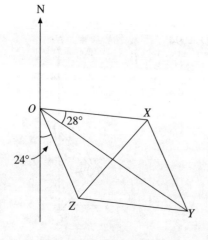

In the diagram, $OXYZ$ is a rhombus.
Calculate the bearings of the following.
(a) X from O
(b) O from Y
(c) Y from Z
(d) X from Y
(e) Z from X

7. *ABCDE* is a regular pentagon, with *O* as the centre. Find the bearing of
   (a) *B* from *A*,
   (b) *C* from *A*,
   (c) *D* from *A*,
   (d) *E* from *A*,
   (e) *O* from *A*,
   (f) *B* from *O*,
   (g) *E* from *O*,
   (h) *D* from *C*.

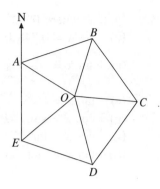

8.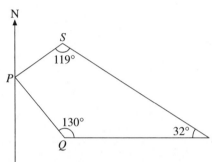

   In the diagram, *R* is due east of *Q*. Calculate the bearing of
   (a) *P* from *Q*,
   (b) *S* from *P*,
   (c) *R* from *S*.

9. In the diagram, *XY* is a tangent to the circle, with centre *O*, at *U*.

   $T\hat{U}Y = 54°$ and $S\hat{T}U = 60°$.
   Find the bearings of the following.
   (a) *S*, *T* and *U* from *O*
   (b) *O* from *S*, *T* and *U*
   (c) *S* from *U*

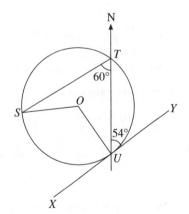

10. Three points *P*, *Q* and *R* are such that the bearing of *Q* from *P* is 27°, the bearing of *R* from *Q* is 155° and *PQ* = *QR*. Find the bearing of
    (a) *P* from *Q*,
    (b) *Q* from *R*,
    (c) *R* from *P*.

11. Express the following in terms of trigonometrical ratios of acute angles.
    (a) tan 142°
    (b) cos 123°
    (c) sin 111°
    (d) −cos 99°
    (e) −tan 102° sin 91°
    (f) sin 165° cos 156° tan 147°

12. Find x, where $0° \leqslant x \leqslant 180°$. Give your answers correct to one decimal place.

    (a) $\sin x = 0.848\ 0$ **(b)** $\cos x = -0.916\ 0$

    (c) $\sin x = \dfrac{1}{\sqrt{2}}$ **(d)** $\cos x = -\dfrac{5}{13}$

    (e) $\tan x = -\sqrt{3}$ **(f)** $\sin x = \cos 35°$

    (g) $\cos x = \sin 142°$ **(h)** $\tan x = -\cos 125°$

    (i) $\cos x = \tan 171°$ **(j)** $\tan x = -\sin 45°$

    (k) $\tan x = -\tan 35°$

13. Given that the coordinates of P and Q are $(8, 15)$ and $(-3, 4)$ respectively, find the value of

    (a) $\sin A$,

    (b) $\tan B$,

    (c) $\tan A \cos B$,

    (d) $\dfrac{\cos A}{\sin B}$.

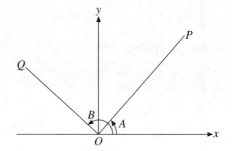

14. In the figure, $A\hat{B}C = 90°$, $BC = 1$ and $AC = \sqrt{5}$.

    (a)   Calculate AB.

    (b)   Write down the value of

         (i) $\sin C\hat{A}B$,

         (ii) $\tan A\hat{C}B$,

       (iii) $\cos A\hat{C}D$.

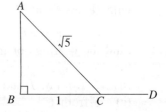

15. In the figure, find

    (a) a if $\hat{A} = 34°$, $b = 7$, $c = 9.5$,

    (b) b if $\hat{A} = 47°$, $\hat{C} = 22°$, $a = 24$, $c = 16$,

    (c) $\hat{C}$ if $a = 60$, $b = 40$, $c = 30$,

    (d) $\hat{B}$ if $a = 16$, $b = 21$, $c = 10$,

    (e) $\hat{B}$ if $\hat{C} = 125°$, $b = 10$, $c = 12$,

    (f) $\hat{A}$ if $\hat{B} = 29°$, $a = 7.5$, $b = 4$ and BC is the longest side,

    (g) c if $\hat{B} = 44°$, $\hat{C} = 49°$, $b = 12$,

(h) a if $\hat{B} = 128°$, $\hat{C} = 30°$, $c = 50$,

(i)   area of $\triangle ABC$ if $\hat{A} = 63°$, $b = 3.7$, $c = 5.4$,

(j) b if $a = 4.9$, $\hat{C} = 97°$, area of $\triangle ABC = 52.8$,

(k) $\hat{C}$ if $a = 13$, $b = 15$, area of $\triangle ABC = 96$ and $\hat{A} + \hat{B} > \hat{C}$.

16.   In the diagram, $AB = AD = CD = 10$ cm
and $A\hat{D}C = 130°$. Calculate
(a)   the area of $\triangle ABC$,
(b)   the length of BD using the sine rule,
(c)   the length of AC using the cosine rule.

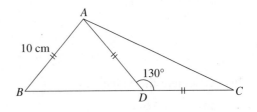

17.

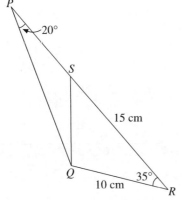

Find the length of
(a) PQ,
(b) PS,
(c) QS.

18.   In the figure, $W\hat{X}Y = 18°$, $X\hat{W}Y = 66°$, $WY = 3$ cm and $WZ = 8$ cm.
Calculate
(a) XW,
(b) YZ,
(c) $W\hat{Z}Y$,
(d) $X\hat{Y}Z$,
(e)   area of $\triangle WYZ$.

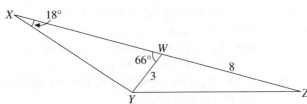

19. In the figure, AC = 8 cm, CD = 5 cm, DE = 10 cm and $A\hat{C}D$ = 132°. Using as much of the information given below as is necessary, calculate

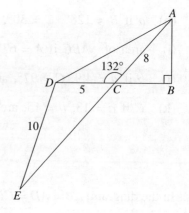

  (a) AD^2,
  (b) BC,
  (c) $\sin C\hat{E}D$,
  (d) area of $\triangle ACD$.
  [$\sin 48°$ = 0.743, $\cos 48°$ = 0.669, $\tan 48°$ = 1.11]

20. Calculate the value of

  (a) $\cos A\hat{B}C$,
  (b) $\cos A\hat{C}D$, giving your answer as a fraction in its lowest terms.

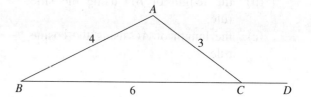

21. Find, giving your answer as a fraction in its lowest terms, the value of

  (a) $\sin A\hat{B}C$ when $\sin A\hat{C}B = \dfrac{2}{9}$,

  (b) $\sin A\hat{C}D$ when $\sin A\hat{B}C = \dfrac{6}{11}$.

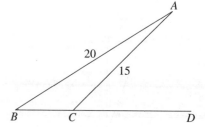

22. A man walks from a point P to a point Q, which is 100 m due east of a building, B.

  (a) Given that $B\hat{P}Q$ = 60° and $B\hat{Q}P$ = 50°, calculate
    (i) the bearing of P from Q,
    (ii) the bearing of B from P,
    (iii) the distance PQ,
    (iv) the shortest distance between the building and the man during his journey from P to Q.
  (b) If the angle of elevation of the top of the building from Q is 65°, find the height of the building.

54

23. The cross-section of a pedestrian underpass is the major segment of a circle, centre O, as shown in the diagram.

Given that $A\hat{O}B = 100°$ and $OA = OB = 1.5$ m, calculate

(a) AB,

(b) the area of $\triangle AOB$,

(c) the area of the major segment,

(d) the amount of air space in the underpass if it is 70 m long.

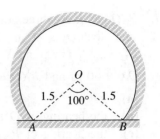

24. From the top of a building 35 m high, the angle of depression of a car A due north of it is $42°$ and the angle of depression of a car B due west of it is $57°$. How far apart are the cars A and B?

25. A, B, C and D are points on level ground. $AD = 38$ m, $CD = 50$ m, B is 15 m due east of A and C is 20 m due north of A.

Calculate

(a) $A\hat{B}C$,

(b) $C\hat{A}D$,

(c) the bearing of B from C,

(d) the bearing of D from A.

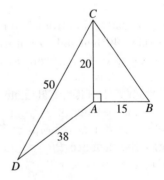

26. A, B and C are three points on level ground. $AC = 60$ m, $BC = 100$ m and $A\hat{C}B = 80°$.

(a) Calculate the distance AB.

(b) A vertical mast stands at the point C and the angle of elevation of the top of the mast from each of the points A and B is known. If the smaller of these angles of elevation is $18°$, calculate the height of the mast.

(c) If C is north of A, calculate

   (i) the bearing of B from C,

   (ii) the distance that B is east of C.

27. P, Q and R are three points on level ground such that Q is 80 m due east of P and $PQ = QR$. The point X on QR is such that $QX = 30$ m and $P\hat{X}Q = 110°$. Calculate

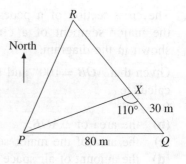

(a) $X\hat{P}Q$,
(b) the bearing of Q from X,
(c) the bearing of R from P,
(d) the distance PR,
(e) the distance PX.

28. Four places P, Q, R and T are such that $PR = PT = QR$. The bearing of T from R is 040°, the bearing of Q from R is 210° and T is due north of P. Calculate the bearing of

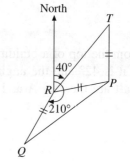

(a) P from R,
(b) Q from P,
(c) R from Q.

29. A ship sails 5 km from P to Q on a bearing of 035°. It then sails 9 km from Q to R on a bearing of 075°. From R, it finally sails to T which is south of R and the bearing of T from Q is 115°. Calculate

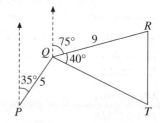

(a) the bearing of P from Q,
(b) how far Q is north of P,
(c) the distance PR,
(d) the distance RT,
(e) the angle of depression of the ship from a lighthouse 52 m high and 20 km from T.

30. The figure $ABCDEFGH$ is a cuboid in which $DC = 3$ cm, $AD = 4$ cm and $AE = 2$ cm. Find

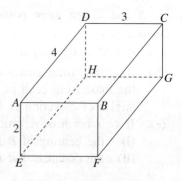

(a) $A\hat{G}E$,
(b) $A\hat{F}G$,
(c) $Y\hat{X}E$ where X is the midpoint of AE and Y is the midpoint of HG.

31. The diagram shows a pyramid with a rectangular base *ABCD* and vertex *V*. The slant edges *VA*, *VB*, *VC* and *VD* are equal and the diagonals of the base intersect at *M*. The midpoint of *AD* is *N*. *AC* = 15 cm, *BC* = 9 cm and *VM* = 10 cm. Calculate

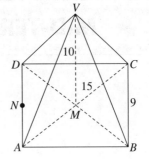

   (a) *AB*,
   (b) *VA*,
   (c) $V\hat{N}M$,
   (d) $B\hat{V}C$,
   (e) $V\hat{D}B$.

32. In the figure, *AB* = *AX*, $B\hat{A}X$ = 20° and $X\hat{A}C$ = 35°. Find the bearing of

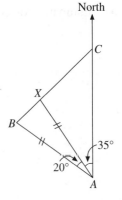

   (a) *C* from *X*,
   (b) *B* from *C*,
   (c) *A* from *B*,
   (d) *X* from *A*.

33. *A*, *B* and *C* are three points on level ground. The bearing of *B* from *A* is 070° and the bearing of *C* from *A* is 110°. It is given that *C* is 5 km due south of *B*.

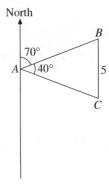

   (a) Find
        (i)   the distance of *C* from *A*,
        (ii) the shortest distance from *B* to *AC*.
   (b) Another point *D* is 5 km due east of *C*. Find
        (i)   the bearing of *D* from *B*,
        (ii) the distance *BD*.

MID-TERM ASSESSMENT

Time : $1\frac{1}{2}$ hours

Marks : 52

Section I

Answer **ALL** questions in this section.
All working must be clearly shown in the space provided.
Calculators are **NOT** allowed in this section.

1. **(a)** Estimate, correct to 1 significant figure, the value of
$$\frac{10.9 \times 0.048\ 3}{219}.$$
[2]

Ans _____

(b) Find the value of $\dfrac{(15 \times 10^{-3})^2}{3}$ and express the answer in the standard form.
[2]

Ans _____

58

2. **(a)** Simplify $\dfrac{2x}{9 - x^2} + \dfrac{3}{3 + x}$. [3]

   (b) Hence, or otherwise, solve $\dfrac{2x}{9 - x^2} + \dfrac{3}{3 + x} = 1$. [3]

   Ans (a) _____

   (b) _____

3. $10 800 is shared among 3 business partners A, B and C in the ratio $7 : 3 : 2$.
   (a) Find the angle of the sector in a pie-chart that represents A's share. [2]
   (b) What is the percentage of the share that B received? [2]
   (c) How much more than C did A get? [2]

   Ans (a) _____

   (b) _____

   (c) _____

4. Evaluate **(a)** $\dfrac{4^{\frac{1}{3}} \times 3^{-\frac{1}{3}}}{6^{-\frac{1}{3}}}$, [3]

(b) $\left(\dfrac{4}{3}\right)^{-2} + \left(\dfrac{81}{16}\right)^{\frac{1}{4}}$. [3]

Ans (a) _____

(b) _____

5. (a) Simplify $x^{\frac{3}{2}} y^{\frac{3}{4}} \div \dfrac{x^{\frac{2}{3}}}{y^{-\frac{1}{12}}}$. [2]

Ans _____

(b) Given that $p^{-2} = 3q^{\frac{1}{3}}$, find p when $q = 27$. [2]

Ans _____

6. Factorise completely:

(a) $50a^3 - 2a$ [2]

(b) $7 - 2x^2 - 13x$ [2]

Ans (a) _____

(b) _____

7. **(a)** Given that $\dfrac{3}{3x - p} = \dfrac{2}{q + 4}$, make x the subject. [2]

Ans _____

(b) Solve the quadratic equation $2x^2 - 5x = 1$.

[Given $\sqrt{1.7} = 1.304$, $\sqrt{0.17} = 0.412$, $\sqrt{3.3} = 1.817$ and $\sqrt{0.33} = 0.574$] [4]

Ans _____

8. (a) Find an integer m such that $114 < \dfrac{m^3}{3} < 115$. [2]

Ans _____

(b) List the integer values of x for which

$$3x - 8 < 28 \leqslant 4x - 5.$$ [3]

Ans _____

9. Given that y varies inversely as the square root of $(x - 3)$ and that $y = \dfrac{1}{2}$ when
    $x = 19$, find
    (a) the rule connecting x and y,   [3]
    (b) the value of x when $y = -\dfrac{1}{5}$.   [2]

    Ans (a) _____

    (b) _____

10. A straight line passes through the points $P(1, -1)$, $Q(3, 5)$ and $R(k, 11)$.
    (a) Find the length of PQ.   [2]
    (b) Calculate the value of k.   [2]
    (c) Find the equation of the straight line passing through the midpoint of PQ and
         parallel to the line $2x + y = 1$.   [2]

    Ans (a) _____

    (b) _____

    (c) _____

Time : 1 hour

Marks : 48

Section II

Answer any **FOUR** questions.
Each question carries 12 marks.
Calculators may be used in this section.

1. **(a)** A motorist travelled for 6 days from Monday to Saturday.
    (i) If he travelled a distance of 96 km, correct to the nearest km, per day from Monday to Thursday and 100 km, correct to the nearest km, on Friday, find the limits between which the total distance he travelled during the first 5 days must lie.   [3]
    (ii) If the total distance travelled from Monday to Saturday was 564 km, correct to the nearest km, between what limits must the distance travelled on Saturday lie?   [3]

Ans (a) (i) _____

                    (ii) _____

(b) The mass of a wooden box is 437.0 g, correct to the nearest 0.1 g. What is the minimum possible volume of the box if the density of wood is 0.9 g/cm^3, correct to the nearest 0.1 g/cm^3? Give your answer correct to one decimal place. [3]

Ans _____

(c) Solve the inequality $x - 2 \leqslant \frac{x}{4} + 1 < \frac{3}{2}x$. [3]

Ans _____

2. The equation of a straight line is of the form $y = mx + c$, where m is the gradient and c is the y-intercept.
   (a) Given that the gradient of the line is a and that the line passes through the point $(a, 0)$, find, in terms of a,
      (i) the value of c,
      (ii) the equation of the line. [4]

Ans (i) _____

(ii) _____

   (b) Given further that the line passes through the point $(5, 6)$, form an equation in a and show that it reduces to $a^2 - 5a + 6 = 0$. [3]

   (c) Solve the equation $a^2 - 5a + 6 = 0$ and hence, find the two possible equations of the line. [5]

Ans _____

_____

3. (a) In the figure, $AC = 7$, $BC = 5$, $CD = 8$ and $AD = 10$.
Find the bearing of D from A. [2]

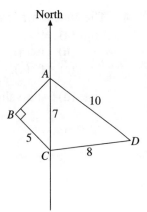

Ans _____

(b) In the diagram, $AD = 3$ cm, $AX = 6$ cm, $BX = 4$ cm, $A\hat{D}C = 90°$, $D\hat{A}C = 75°$, $A\hat{X}B = 120°$ and $X\hat{B}C = 50°$.
Find the perimeter and area of the quadrilateral $ABCD$. [10]

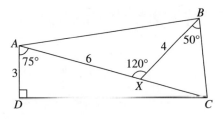

Ans _____ cm

_____ cm^2

4. The function f is denoted by $f(x) = x^2 - 6x + 9$, $x \geqslant 3$.

Find **(a)** f(9), [2]

   (b) $f^{-1}(4)$, [3]

   (c) $f^{-1}(x)$, [3]

   (d) the value of x for which $f(x) = \frac{1}{2}x$. [4]

Ans (a) _____

(b) _____

(c) _____

(d) _____

5. (a) Complete the following table of values for $y = x^3 - 3x + 2$.

x	-2	$-1\frac{1}{2}$	-1	0	1	$1\frac{1}{2}$	2	
y		3.1	4	2	0	0.9		[2]

(b) Taking 2 cm to represent 1 unit on the x-axis and the y-axis, draw the graph of $y = x^3 - 3x + 2$ for $-2 \leqslant x \leqslant 2$. [3]

(c) Using the graph, estimate
   (i) the values of x for which $2x^3 - 6x = 1$. [3]

Ans _____

   (ii) the area, in square units, between the graph, the x-axis and the lines $x = -1$ and $x = 1$. [2]

Ans _____

(d) By drawing a tangent, find the gradient of the curve $y = x^3 - 3x + 2$ at the point where $x = -\frac{1}{2}$. [2]

Ans _____

CHAPTER 8

Symmetry Properties of a Circle

1. Given that AOB is a straight line and O is the centre of the circle. Find the values of x and y.

   (a)

   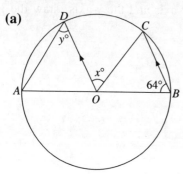

   (b)

   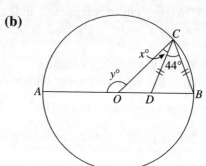

2. Given that AOD is a straight line and O is the centre of the circle, find the values of x, y and z in each case.

   (a)

   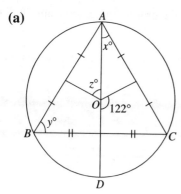

   (b)

   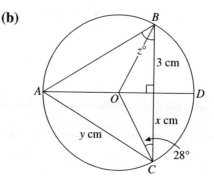

3.

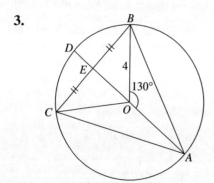

In the figure, AOD is a straight line and O is the centre of the circle. Given that $A\hat{O}B = 130°$, $OB = 4$ cm and $BE = CE$, calculate

(a) $O\hat{C}B$,

(b) DE,

(c) AB.

4. Given that O is the centre of the circle,
   (a) write down the value of x and of y,
   (b) find the area of the circle.

$\left(\text{Use } \pi = \dfrac{22}{7}\right)$

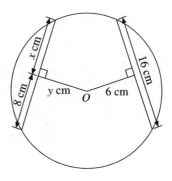

5. In the figure, O is the centre of the circle. Given that $OD = OE = 3$ cm and $AD = 4$ cm, find
   (a) BE,
   (b) the length of the longest chord,
   (c) the area of the triangle ABC.

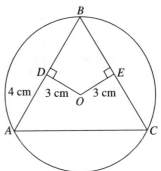

6. Given that O is the centre of the circle and PQ and PR are tangents to the circle at Q and R respectively, find the value of x and of y in each case.

(a)

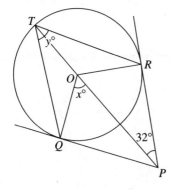

(b)

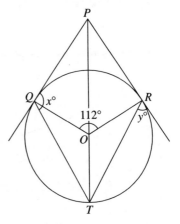

(c)

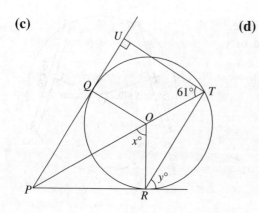

(d)

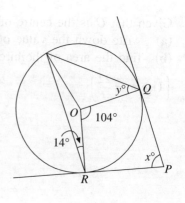

(e)

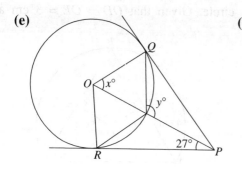

(f)

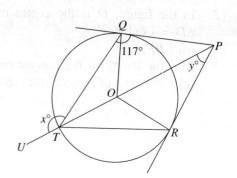

7. In the figure, AB, AC and BC are tangents to the circle, with centre O, at D, E and F respectively. Find x and y.

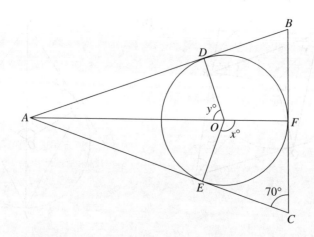

8. In the figure, *AB*, *AC*, *BD* and *CD* are tangents to the circle at *P*, *Q*, *R* and *S* respectively and *O* is the centre of the circle. Calculate the value of *x* and of *y*.

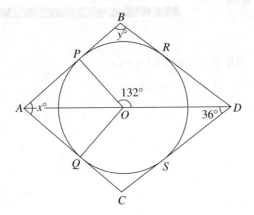

9. Given that *O* is the centre of the circle, *AC* is the tangent to the circle at *B* and *AOD* is a straight line, find *x* and *y*.

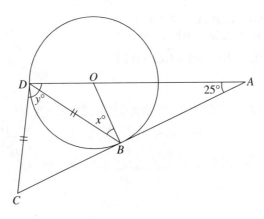

CHAPTER 9
Angle Properties of a Circle

1. In the diagram, AB is a diameter of the circle with centre O, $B\hat{A}P = 22°$ and $A\hat{R}P = 41°$. Calculate

   (a) $R\hat{A}B$,

   (b) $A\hat{Q}P$,

   (c) $B\hat{O}P$.

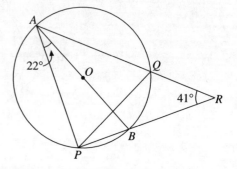

2. In the diagram, A, B, C, D and E are points on the circle with centre O. $AB = AE$, $A\hat{C}E = 28°$ and $E\hat{D}C = 113°$. Calculate

   (a) $B\hat{A}E$,

   (b) $A\hat{B}C$.

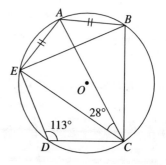

3. In the diagram, O is the centre of the circle, POR is a straight line, $Q\hat{P}R = 53°$ and $R\hat{P}S = 10°$. Calculate

   (a) $Q\hat{R}S$,

   (b) $P\hat{Q}S$.

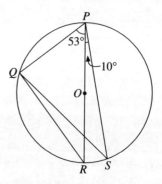

4. In the diagram, *CB* and *CD* are tangents to the circle with centre *O*, *AOC* is a straight line and $O\hat{C}B = 34°$. Calculate

(a) $C\hat{D}B$,

(b) $B\hat{O}D$,

(c) $A\hat{B}O$.

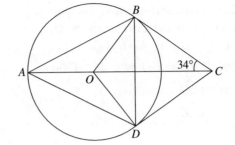

5. *ABCD* is a cyclic quadrilateral and *ADE* is a straight line. Given that $B\hat{C}A = 65°$, $C\hat{A}D = 62°$ and $A\hat{B}D = 18°$, calculate

(a) $B\hat{A}D$,

(b) $C\hat{D}E$.

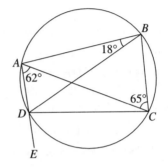

6. *AOD* is a diameter of the circle, centre *O*. Given that $B\hat{D}A = 18°$ and $B\hat{D}C = 38°$, calculate

(a) $A\hat{B}O$,

(b) $B\hat{O}C$,

(c) $B\hat{C}D$.

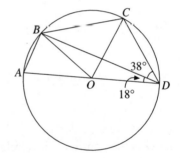

7. In the diagram, *AOC* is a diameter of the circle, centre *O*. *RST* is the tangent at *S*. Given that $A\hat{S}O = 38°$ and $B\hat{A}C = 26°$, calculate

(a) $C\hat{S}T$,

(b) $A\hat{B}S$,

(c) $B\hat{S}O$,

(d) $B\hat{C}S$.

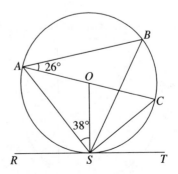

75

8. In the diagram, *RST* is the tangent to the circle, centre *O*, at *S*. *AOS* is a straight line, *BO* // *RT* and $O\hat{R}S = 46°$. Find

(a) $O\hat{C}A$,

(b) $B\hat{A}C$.

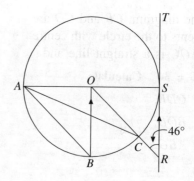

9. In the diagram, *CDE* is a straight line and *A*, *B*, *C* and *D* are points on the circle. Given that $B\hat{C}D = 44°$, find the value of *x* and of *y*.

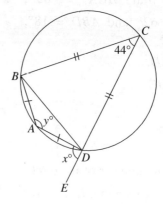

10. Given that *O* is the centre of the circle and *RST* is the tangent to the circle at *S*. Find the value of the unknown marked angles in each case.

(a)

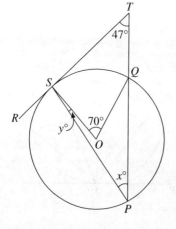

(b)

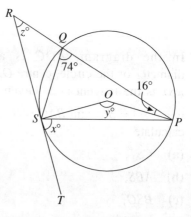

11. Given that *AOB* is a diameter of the circle, centre *O* and *RST* is the tangent to the circle at *S*. Find the value of *x* and of *y* in each case.

(a)

(b)

12. In the diagram, *AOC* and *BOS* are diameters of the circle centre *O*, *RST* is the tangent to the circle at *S* and *AÔS* = 124°. Calculate

(a) *AŜT*,

(b) *AR̂T*.

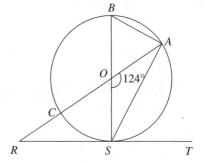

13. In the diagram, *O* is the centre of the circle, *AĈB* = 54° and *BCE* is a straight line. Find the value of *x* and of *y*.

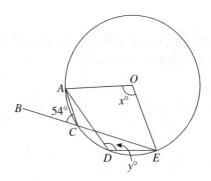

14. In the diagram, *A*, *B*, *C*, *D* and *E* are points on the circle, *AD* is parallel to *BC*, *AB̂E* = 39° and *AD̂C* = 62°. Find the value of *x* and of *y*.

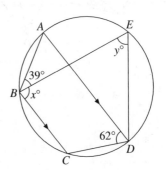

15. In the figure, *BOD* is a diameter of the circle with centre *O*, $C\hat{O}D = 92°$ and $A\hat{B}D = 65°$. Find the value of *x* and of *y*.

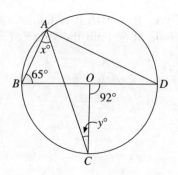

16. *RST* is the tangent to the circle at *S*. Find the value of *x* and of *y* in each case.

(a)

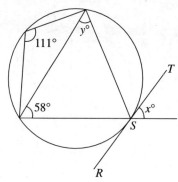

(b)

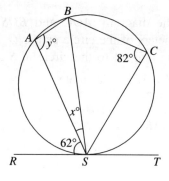

17. Given that *O* is the centre of the circle and *AOB* is a straight line, find the value of *x* and of *y* in each case.

(a)

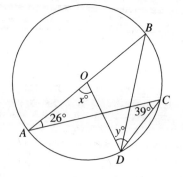

(b)

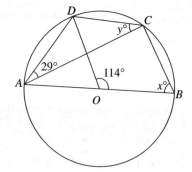

Time : 1 hour
Marks : 50

1. Given that AB and AC are tangents to the circle at B and C respectively and O is the centre of the circle, find the value of x and of y in each case.

(a) [4]

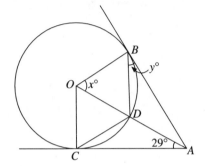

Ans $x =$ _____

$y =$ _____

(b) [4]

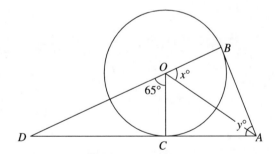

Ans $x =$ _____

$y =$ _____

79

2. In the figure, O is the centre of the circle of radius 4 cm. AB and AC are tangents to the circle at B and C respectively and $AB = AC = BC$. Find

    (a) $O\hat{C}B$,
    (b) OD,
    (c) AC.

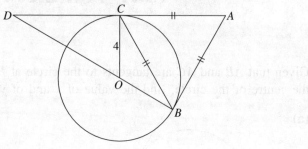

[5]

Ans (a) _____

     (b) _____

     (c) _____

3. AC is the tangent to the circle at B. BOE is a straight line and O is the centre of the circle. Find the value of x and of y. [4]

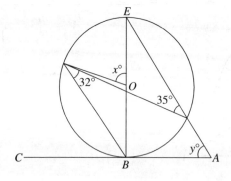

Ans x = _____

     y = _____

4. O is the centre of the circle. Find the value of x and of y. [4]

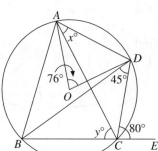

Ans $x = $ _____

$y = $ _____

5. Given that AOB is a straight line and O is the centre of the circle. Find the values of x and y.

(a) [4]

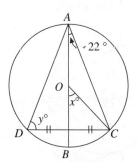

Ans $x = $ _____

$y = $ _____

(b) [4]

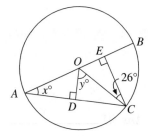

Ans $x = $ _____

$y = $ _____

6. In the figures, *AB* and *AC* are tangents to the circle at *B* and *C* respectively and *O* is the centre of the circle.

    (a)   Given that *AE* = 5 cm and *AB* = 10 cm, find the radius of the circle.   [2]

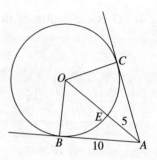

Ans _____

    (b)   Given that *OB* = 3 cm and *OÂB* = 20°, find the length of

        (i)   *AB*,

        (ii)   *AD*,

        (iii)   *CD*.   [5]

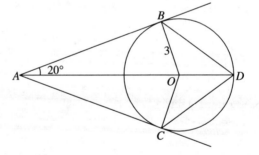

Ans (i) _____

        (ii) _____

        (iii) _____

(c) Given that OB = 10 cm and AC = 24 cm, calculate

    (i) AE,

    (ii) $A\hat{O}B$,

    (iii) the area of the shaded region.   [6]

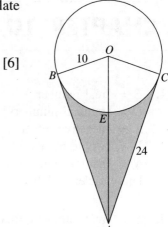

Ans (i) _____

(ii) _____

(iii) _____

7. Given that O is the centre of the circle, find the value of x and of y in each case.

(a)

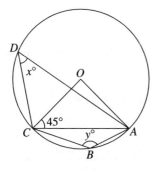

[4]

(b)

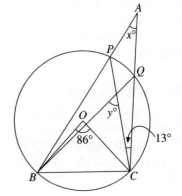

[4]

Ans (a) x = _____

y = _____

Ans (b) x = _____

y = _____

CHAPTER 10, 11 Sets

1. $\mathcal{E}$ = {real numbers}
   Q = {rational numbers}
   Z = {negative integers}
   W = {whole numbers}
   N = {natural numbers}
   Draw a clearly labelled Venn diagram to represent these sets.

2. $\mathcal{E}$ = {real numbers greater than 2 but not more than 12}
   A = {odd numbers}
   B = {even numbers}
   C = {prime numbers}
   D = {square numbers}
   Mark the members of these sets clearly on a Venn diagram.

3. $\mathcal{E}$ = {quadrilaterals}
   P = {parallelograms}
   R = {rectangles}
   H = {rhombuses}
   T = {trapeziums}
   Illustrate with a Venn diagram the relation between the sets $\mathcal{E}$, P, R, H and T.

4. $\mathcal{E}$ = {all triangles}
   A = {equilateral triangles}
   B = {isosceles triangles}
   C = {right-angled triangles}
   D = {obtuse-angled triangles}
   Draw a Venn diagram to illustrate the sets $\mathcal{E}$, A, B, C and D.

5. Given that $B \cap C = \phi$, $B \subset A$ and $A \cap C = C$, draw a Venn diagram to illustrate the sets A, B and C.
   Hence, or otherwise, simplify
   (a) $B \cap C'$,
   (b) $A \cup B \cup C$.

6. The sets L, M and N are such that $n(L \cap N) = 0$ and $M \subset L$. Draw a Venn diagram to show the relation between the sets L, M and N. Hence, or otherwise, simplify
   (a) $M \cap N$,
   (b) $L \cap M$,
   (c) $M' \cap N$,
   (d) $N' \cap (L \cup M)$.

7. In the Venn diagram, shade
   (a) $(A' \cap C') \cup B$,

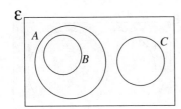

   (b) $C \cup (A \cap B)$.

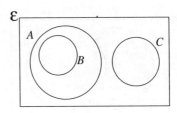

8. In the Venn diagram, shade
   (a) $A \cap (B \cup C)'$,

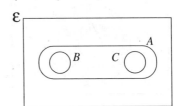

   (b) $(A \cup C) \cap B'$,

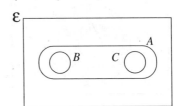

   (c) $A \cap C$,

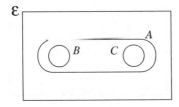

   (d) $A \cup B$.

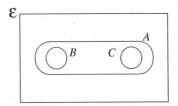

9. In the Venn diagram, shade
   (a) $(P \cap Q) \cup R$,

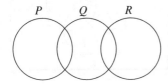

   (b) $(P \cup Q) \cap R$,

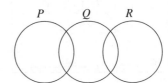

   (c) $(P \cup R)' \cap Q$,

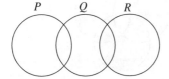

   (d) $P \cup R \cap Q'$.

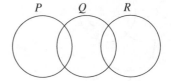

10. Write, in set notation, the set indicated by the shaded region in each of the following diagrams.

(a)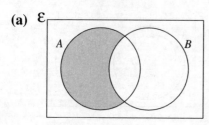

(b)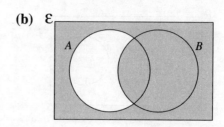

(c)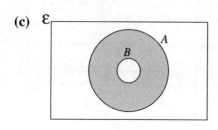

(d)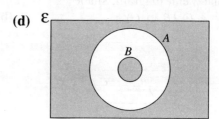

(e)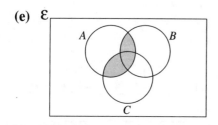

(f)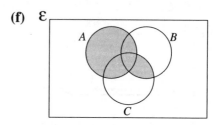

(g)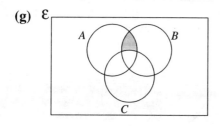

(h)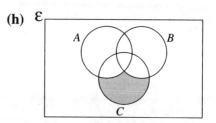

(i)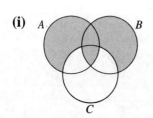

(j)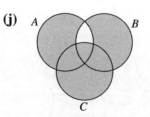

11. Shade, on separate diagrams, the regions that represent the following sets.

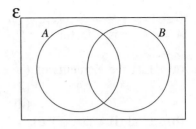

   (a) **(i)** $(A \cup B)'$
       (ii) $A' \cap B$

   (b) **(i)** $A \cap B$

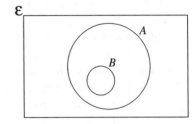

       (ii) $(A \cup B)'$

   (c) **(i)** $A \cap (B \cup C')$

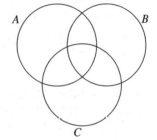

       (ii) $A \cup (B \cap C')$
       (iii) $A' \cap (B \cup C)$
       (iv) $A \cup B \cup C'$
       (v) $A' \cap B' \cup C$
       (vi) $A' \cap (B' \cup C)$
       (vii) $A' \cup B' \cup C$
       (viii) $A' \cup (B' \cap C)$

12. $\mathcal{E} = \{e, f, g, h, i, j, k, l\}$
$A = \{e, f, i, j\}$
$B = \{i, j, k, l\}$
$C = \{f, g, h, k\}$
   (a) Find **(i)** $n(B \cap C)$,
           (ii) $n(A \cap B')$.
   (b) List the elements of **(i)** $(A \cup C)'$,
                     (ii) $(B \cup C) \cap A$.

13. $\mathcal{E} = \{p, q, r, s, t, u, v, w, x, y\}$
$L = \{p, q, r, s, t\}$
$M = \{s, t, u, v, w\}$
$N = \{u, v\}$
Illustrate with a Venn diagram the relation between the sets $\mathcal{E}$, L, M and N. Use your diagram, or otherwise, to list the members of $(L \cup N) \cap M$.

14. $\mathcal{E} = \{x : 3 \leqslant x \leqslant 17, x$ is an integer$\}$
    $A = \{x : x$ is a factor of 42$\}$
    $B = \{x : 3x - 7 < 29\}$
    (a) List the elements of (i) A,
                              (ii) B',
                              (iii) $A \cap B$.
    (b) Find (i)   n($A' \cap B$),
             (ii) n($A \cup B$)'.

15. It is given that n($\mathcal{E}$) = 100 and that A and B are two sets such that n($A \cap B$) = 12,
    n(A) = 36 and n(B') = 72.
    (a) Draw a Venn diagram to illustrate the given information.
    (b) Find (i)   n($A \cap B'$),
             (ii) n($A' \cap B$),
             (iii) n($A \cup B$)',
             (iv) n(A'),
             (v)   n($A \cup B'$),
             (vi) n($A' \cup B$).

16. $\mathcal{E} = \{x : 22 < 3x - 2 \leqslant x + 46, x \in Z\}$
    $A = \{x : x$ is a multiple of 3$\}$
    $B = \{x : x$ is a multiple of 4$\}$
    $C = \{x : x$ is a multiple of 6$\}$
    (a) List the elements of (i) $A \cap B \cup C$,
                              (ii) $(A \cup B \cup C)'$.
    (b) Find (i)   n($A \cap B \cap C$),
             (ii) n[$(A \cup B)' \cap C$].

17. $\mathcal{E} = \{x : x$ is an integer and $5 \leqslant x < 16\}$
    $A = \{x : x$ is a factor of 30$\}$
    $B = \{x : x$ is divisible by 5$\}$
    $C = \{x : x$ is a multiple of 2$\}$
    (a) Mark the members of these sets clearly on a Venn diagram.
    (b) (i)   Hence, or otherwise, list the elements of $A \cap (B \cup C)$.
         (ii) Find n($A' \cap B'$).

18. $\mathcal{E} = \{$natural numbers not more than 18$\}$
    $A = \{$odd numbers$\}$
    $B = \{$square numbers$\}$
    (a) List the elements of $A' \cup B$.
    (b) Find n($A \cap B'$).

19. Two sets P and Q are such that $n(P) = 35$ and $n(Q) = 20$. Given that $n(\mathcal{E}) = 100$, find the greatest and least possible value of
(a) $n(P \cap Q)$,
(b) $n(P \cup Q)'$.

20. It is given that $n(\mathcal{E}) = 50$, $n(A) = 39$ and $n(B) = 24$.
(a) Find the smallest and largest possible value of
    (i) $n(A \cap B)$,
    (ii) $n(A \cup B)'$.
(b) If $A \cap B' = 20$, find the value of
    (i) $A' \cap B$,
    (ii) $(A \cup B)'$.

21. A, B and C are three sets and the elements are as shown in the Venn diagram. The universal set $\mathcal{E} = A \cup B \cup C$.
(a) State the value of $n[(B \cup C)']$.
(b) Given that $n(B) = 29$, find
    (i) x,
    (ii) $n(\mathcal{E})$,
    (iii) $n[A' \cap (B \cap C)]$.

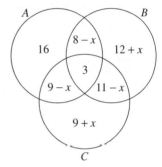

22. It is given that $n(\mathcal{E}) = 100$ and that P and Q are two sets such that $n(P \cap Q) = 9$, $n(P) = 39$ and $n(Q) = 28$. Draw a Venn diagram to illustrate this information and hence, find $n(P' \cap Q')$.

23. A and B are two sets and the number of elements in each subset is shown in the Venn diagram. Given that $n(A) = n(B)$, calculate
(a) x,
(b) $n(A \cup B)$.

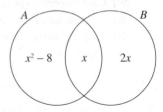

24. In a group of 20 students, all study either Physics or Mathematics or both. If 10 students study Physics and 15 study Mathematics,
(a) find
    (i)   the number of students who study both Physics and Mathematics,
    (ii)   the number of students who study Physics only.
(b) illustrate the results on a Venn diagram.

25. Each of the 30 students in a certain class of a school studies at least one of the languages Japanese, French and German.

Of the 17 students who study Japanese,
   3 also study French and German,
   7 study neither French nor German and
   4 study French but not German.

Of the 13 students who do not study Japanese,
   5 study only German,
   3x study only French and
   x study both German and French.

Show the number of students in each subset on the Venn diagram. Hence, find
(a) the value of x,
(b) the total number of students studying French,
(c) the number of students studying both Japanese and German.

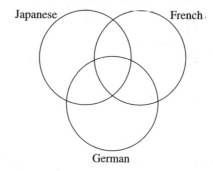

German

26. 100 candidates sat for an examination. Of these, 66 candidates sat for the History paper, 51 sat for the Geography paper and 10 candidates sat for neither the History nor Geography paper. Find
(a) the number of candidates who sat only for the History paper,
(b) the number of candidates who sat either for the History or the Geography paper but not both.

27. A survey was carried out to find out whether 50 families dine out on Saturdays and Sundays.
   23 families said they dine out on Saturdays,
   31 families said they dine out on Sundays,
   6 families said they do not dine out on either day.
By drawing a Venn diagram, or otherwise, calculate
(a) the number of families who dine out on both days,
(b) the number of families who dine out only on Sundays.

90

28. 30 ladies were interviewed to find out whether they wear earrings, bracelet and necklace.

Given that 2 wear all three types of jewellery,
3 wear only earrings and necklace,
4 wear only necklace and bracelet,
x wear only earrings and bracelet,
$x + 3$ wear only earrings,
14 wear earrings,
12 wear necklace and
2 do not wear any of these jewellery,

illustrate this information on a clearly labelled Venn diagram, showing the number in each separate region. Find

(a) the value of x,

(b) the number of ladies who wear bracelet only,

(c) the number of ladies who wear at least 2 of these three types of jewellery.

29. A teacher, during one of her lessons on 'Television Programmes', questioned her 40 students about the channels they watched on a particular evening.

16 students said they watched Channel 5,
18 students watched Channel 8,
17 students watched Channel 12,
9 students watched Channels 5 and 8,
8 students watched Channels 5 and 12

and 7 students watched Channels 8 and 12

If 6 students did not watch any of these channels, find out how many students

(a) watched all the three channels,

(b) watched Channels 5 and 8 but not Channel 12,

(c) watched Channel 12 only.

CHAPTER 12 / Rate of Change and Area under Graph

1. The diagram is the distance-time graph of an object.

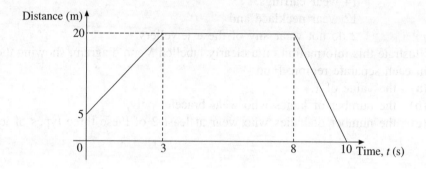

(a) Find the speed of the object for the
    (i) first 3 seconds,
    (ii) next 5 seconds,
    (iii) last 2 seconds.
(b) Find the total distance travelled by the object during the 10 seconds.
(c) Find the average speed of the object during the 10 seconds.
(d) Describe what happened from $t = 3$ to $t = 8$.

2. The diagram is the speed-time graph of an object.

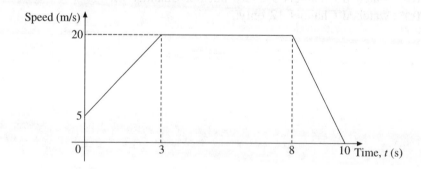

(a) Find the acceleration of the object for the
    (i) first 3 seconds,
    (ii) next 5 seconds,
    (iii) last 2 seconds.
(b) Find the total distance travelled by the object during the 10 seconds.
(c) Find the average speed of the object during the 10 seconds.
(d) Describe what happened from $t = 3$ to $t = 8$.

3. A cyclist travels along a straight road for 20 minutes at a constant speed of 36 km/h. He then gets off and pushes his bicycle for 10 minutes at 7.2 km/h. Using a scale of 2 cm to represent 5 minutes on the horizontal axis and 1 cm to represent 1 km on the vertical axis, draw a distance-time graph and find his average speed for the whole journey.

4.

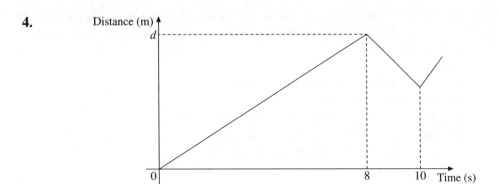

The diagram is the distance-time graph of a particle. The particle starts from rest and moves d m forward at 1.5 m/s in the first 8 seconds. It then moves 5 m backwards in the next 2 seconds; followed by 3 m forward at 1 m/s. Find
(a) the value of d,
(b) the speed when $t = 9$,
(c) the average speed for the whole journey.

5.

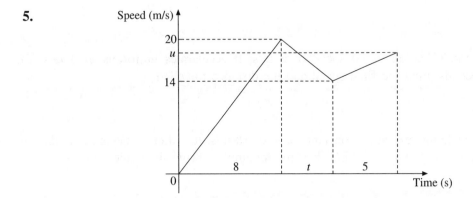

The diagram shows the speed-time graph of part of a car journey. The car starts from rest and steadily accelerates to a speed of 20 m/s in 8 seconds. Due to road repairs, it has to reduce its speed to 14 m/s at a constant acceleration of -1.5 m/s^2 in t seconds. Then the car accelerates uniformly at 0.8 m/s^2 for 5 seconds until it reaches a speed of u m/s. Calculate
(a) the acceleration of the car in the first 8 seconds,
(b) the value of t,
(c) the value of u.

6. On approaching a traffic light junction, a car decelerates uniformly from 18 m/s to 8 m/s in 7 seconds. It continues to decelerate at a different rate until it finally comes to rest after a further 24 seconds. Draw a speed-time graph and find the two rates of change of speed and the distance covered by the car in the 31 seconds.

7. A cyclist starting from a point A travels 300 m due east to a point B at a constant speed of 6 m/s. He rests at B for 10 seconds and then travels 200 m due west to a point C for 40 seconds.
   (a) Find
       (i)   the time taken to travel from A to B,
       (ii) the speed from B to C,
       (iii) the average speed during the last 50 seconds,
       (iv) the average speed for the whole journey.
   (b) Draw the distance-time graph of the cyclist.

8. A particle moving in a straight line with constant acceleration has a speed of 10 m/s at one instant. Six seconds later, it has a speed of 2 m/s. Find its acceleration.

9. A train starts from rest and accelerates at a constant rate for 30 seconds, reaching a speed of 24 m/s. Find the acceleration and the distance covered by the train in the 30 seconds.

10. A particle has an initial speed of 2 m/s. It accelerates uniformly at 3 m/s^2 for 5 seconds. Find the final speed and the distance travelled.

11. A vehicle moves with a constant speed of 18 m/s. It is then subjected to a uniform retardation of 0.6 m/s^2. Find the time required to bring the vehicle to rest.

12. A car takes 70 seconds to travel between two sets of traffic lights. Starting from rest at the first set, the car accelerated at a constant rate for 50 seconds, reaching a speed of 12 m/s. It then uniformly decelerates to rest at the second set of traffic light in a further 20 seconds.
    (a) Draw a speed-time graph for the car.
    (b) Calculate
        (i) the acceleration of the car during the first 50 seconds,
        (ii) the distance between the two sets of traffic lights.

13.

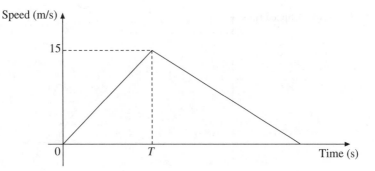

The diagram shows the speed-time graph of a particle. The particle starts from rest and accelerates for T seconds until it reaches a speed of 15 m/s. It then begins to slow down with a uniform retardation of 3 m/s² until it comes to rest.

(a) Calculate how long it will take for the particle to come to rest under the retardation.

(b) Calculate the value of T, given that the total distance travelled is 60 m.

14. A car starts from rest and accelerates steadily at 1.5 m/s² until it reaches a speed of 30 m/s. It maintains a constant speed of 30 m/s for 12 seconds and is then brought to rest in a further 10 seconds.

(a) Draw a speed-time graph for the car.

(b) Find
  (i) the acceleration of the car during the last 10 seconds,
  (ii) the average speed of the car during the last 22 seconds.

15. A particle travels at a speed of 10 m/s. It then decelerates from this speed at 3 m/s for 2 seconds. It maintains a constant speed for 2 seconds before coming to rest in a further 2 seconds.

(a) Draw a speed-time graph for the whole journey.

(b) Find
  (i) the retardation during the last 2 seconds,
  (ii) the distance travelled during the 6 seconds.

16. The distance between two bus stops X and Y is 1 680 m. A bus starts from X and accelerates uniformly for 15 s until it reaches its maximum speed of 24 m/s. It maintains this constant speed for some time and then decelerates uniformly to stop at Y after a further 25 seconds.

(a) Draw a sketch in which the speed is plotted against time.

(b) Find the total time taken for the journey from X to Y.

17.

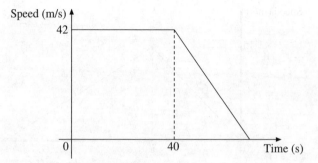

The diagram is the speed-time graph of a car which passes a point A at a uniform speed of 42 m/s. When the brakes are applied 40 seconds later, the car slows down uniformly and comes to a rest at B, which is 2.31 km away from A. Find the time taken to travel from A to B.

18. A vehicle starts from rest and accelerates uniformly at 0.6 m/s² for T s. After attaining a certain speed, a tyre punctures and the brakes are applied to bring the vehicle slowly to rest under a uniform retardation of 1.5 m/s². The whole journey takes 70 seconds.
   (a) Draw a sketch in which the speed is plotted against time.
   (b) Find the value of T and hence find the maximum speed attained.

19. The diagram is the speed-time graph of a particle. The particle starts from rest and moves with an acceleration of 4 m/s² for T seconds until it reaches a speed of 12 m/s. It then maintains a constant speed of 12 m/s for 20 seconds and is brought to rest in a time of 5 seconds with a constant retardation.

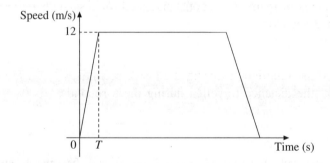

   (a) Find the value of T.
   (b) Calculate
      (i) the retardation,
      (ii) the total distance travelled.

20.

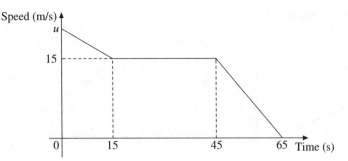

The diagram is the speed-time graph of a car which slows down from a speed of u m/s to 15 m/s in 15 seconds with a constant retardation of 0.4 m/s^2. It then travels at 15 m/s for 30 seconds, after which the brakes are applied and the car is brought to rest in a further 20 seconds.
(a) Find the value of u.
(b) Calculate the retardation during the last 20 seconds.
(c) Calculate
    (i) the speed of the car when $t = 30$,
    (ii) the speed of the car when $t = 49$.
(d) Calculate the distance covered in the 65 seconds.

21.

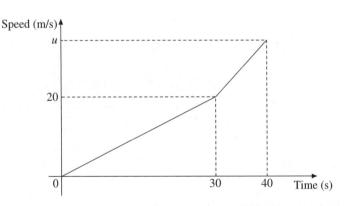

The diagram is the speed-time graph of part of the journey of a motorcycle.
(a) The motorcycle accelerates uniformly from rest to a speed of 20 m/s in 30 seconds. Find
    (i) the acceleration of the motorcycle,
    (ii) the speed of the motorcycle after 18 seconds.
(b) The motorcycle then continues to accelerate at a different rate until it reaches a speed of u m/s after a further 10 seconds. Find the value of u if the distance travelled in the last 10 seconds is 275 m.

22.

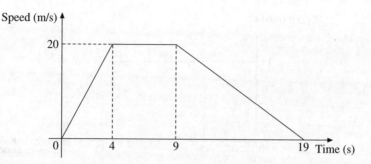

The diagram is the speed-time graph for a particular journey.
(a) Calculate
    (i)   the retardation during the last 10 seconds,
    (ii) the speed when $t = 15$,
    (iii) the total distance travelled.
(b) On the axes in the answer space, sketch
    (i)   the distance-time graph,
    (ii) the acceleration-time graph for the same journey.

Answer (b)   *(i)*

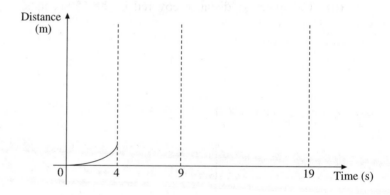

    (ii)

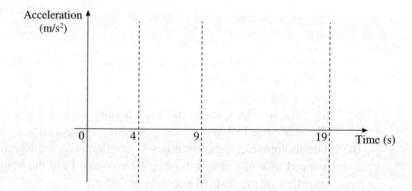

23.

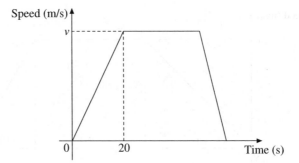

The diagram is the speed-time graph of a train. The train accelerates uniformly for 20 seconds from rest for the first 400 m. It then travels at the acquired constant speed, v m/s, for the next 1.2 km before coming to rest with a uniform retardation. Given that the whole journey takes 1 minute, find

(a) the maximum speed, v m/s,

(b) the time taken to travel the 1.2 km,

(c) the total distance travelled.

24. The diagram is the speed-time graph of a vehicle which is brought to rest in two stages. In the first stage, the speed is uniformly reduced from 70 m/s to 30 m/s in 30 seconds. In the second stage, it is brought to rest under another constant retardation.

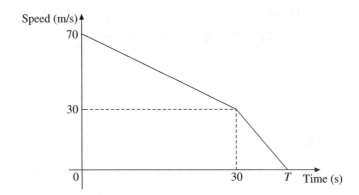

Calculate

(a) the speed of the vehicle after 20 seconds,

(b) the retardation in the first stage,

(c) the value of T, if the total distance travelled in the two stages is 1 650 m.

99

25.

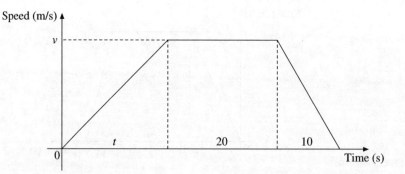

The diagram is the speed-time graph of a car which accelerates uniformly from rest and reaches a speed of v m/s after t seconds. It then travels at v m/s for 20 seconds before coming to rest under a uniform retardation of 4 m/s^2 in a further 10 seconds.
(a) Calculate
    (i)   the maximum speed, v m/s,
    (ii) the distance travelled in the last 30 seconds.
(b)   Given that the total distance travelled is 1 360 m, find the value of t.

26. The diagram is the speed-time graph of a vehicle which accelerates steadily from 5 m/s to 22 m/s in 20 seconds.

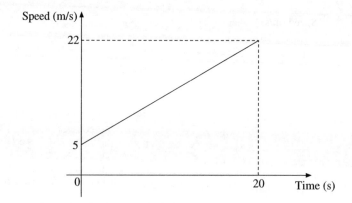

Calculate
(a)   the acceleration,
(b)   the speed after 6 seconds,
(c)   the distance travelled in the 20 seconds.

27.

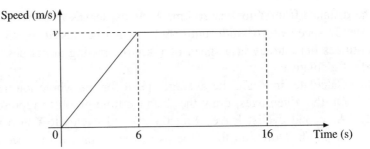

The diagram is the speed-time graph of part of a car journey.
- **(a)** Given that the total distance travelled in the first 16 seconds is 286 m, calculate
  - **(i)** the maximum speed, v m/s,
  - **(ii)** the acceleration of the car in the first 6 seconds.
- **(b)** When $t = 16$, the car begins to slow down with a uniform retardation of 1.1 m/s^2. Calculate how long it will take for the car to come to rest.

28.

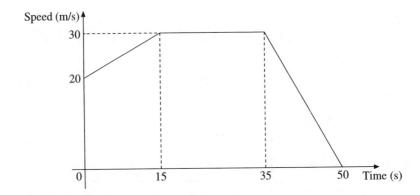

The diagram shows the speed of a particle over a period of 50 seconds. Calculate
- **(a)** the acceleration of the particle during the first 15 seconds,
- **(b)** the distance travelled during the first 20 seconds,
- **(c)** the speed of the particle when $t = 45$,
- **(d)** the values of t for which $v = 24$,
- **(e)** the average speed of the car during the 50 seconds.

29. A car travels 54 km in 45 minutes and for another 40 minutes, it travels at a constant speed of 48 km/h. It then stops to rest for half an hour before travelling the remaining 13 km at a constant speed of 39 km/h. Calculate
- **(a)** the time required for the last part of the journey,
- **(b)** the average speed for the first 45 minutes,
- **(c)** the distance travelled in the first $1\frac{1}{2}$ hours,
- **(d)** the average speed for the whole journey.

30. The distance from X to Y is 26 km. A cyclist leaves X at 08 00 and cycles to Y at a steady speed of 16 km/h, until 09 15, when he rested for 45 minutes. He then continues his journey at a speed of v km/h, arriving at his destination at 10 30.

  (a) Calculate v.

  (b) Calculate, in km/h, the average speed for the whole journey.

  (c) On the given axes, draw the distance-time graph to represent the journey.

  (d) A second cyclist leaves Y at 08 30 and cycles to X at a constant speed of 16 km/h. Draw, on the same axes, the graph for the second cyclist and use your graphs to estimate the distance from X where the cyclists meet each other.

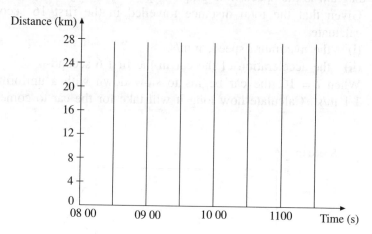

31.

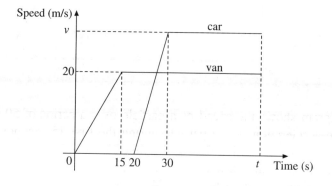

The diagram shows the speed-time graphs of a van and a car. The van starts from rest and moves with uniform acceleration for 15 seconds until it reaches a speed of 20 m/s; it then continues travelling at this speed. Twenty seconds after the van has started on its journey, the car starts from rest at the same place as the van and for 10 seconds, it accelerates at 3 m/s² until it reaches a maximum speed of v m/s.

  (a) Find

  (i) the acceleration of the van,

  (ii) the maximum speed, v m/s, of the car.

  (b) The car catches up with the van after the van has travelled for t seconds. Find

  (i) the value of t,

  (ii) the distance travelled by the van during this time.

Time : 1 hour
Marks : 50

1. ε = {letters of the alphabet}
   A = {letters of the word SINGAPORE}
   B = {letters of the word SPECIAL}
   C = {letters of the word CLEAN}
   (a) Mark the members of the sets clearly on the Venn diagram provided.
   (b) Find **(i)** n($A \cap B$),
         (ii) n($A \cup B \cup C$)'.
   (c) List the elements of the set
       (i) $A \cap B \cap C$,
       (ii) ($A \cap B$) $\cup C$.
   (d) Simplify ($A \cup C$) $\cap B$.　　　　　　　　　　　　　　　　[7]

   Ans *(a)*

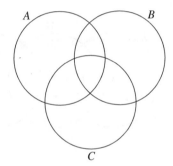

   (b) (i) _____

   (ii) _____

   (c) (i) _____

   (ii) _____

   (d) _____

2. Three sets P, Q and R satisfy the following conditions:

$$P \cap Q \neq \phi, \quad n(P \cap R) = 0, \quad R \subset Q$$

Draw and label a Venn diagram to illustrate these sets. [4]

Ans

3. L, M and N are three sets and $\mathcal{E} = L \cup M \cup N$. The number of members in each subset is shown in the Venn diagram. Given that $n(L) = 39$ and $n(L \cup M)' = L \cap M$, find
   (a) x and y,
   (b) $n(L \cup N)'$,
   (c) $n(\mathcal{E})$. [4]

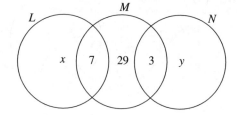

Ans (a) $x = $ _____

$y = $ _____

(b) _____

(c) _____

4. $\mathcal{E}$ is the set of points inside the triangle XYZ.

The subsets A, B and C are defined as follows:

A = {points inside the triangle XYR}

B = {points inside the triangle PYZ}

C = {points inside the triangle TYZ}

Shade the region which represents

(a) $A \cap B \cap C$, **(b)** $(A \cup B)'$. [4]

Ans (a)

(b)

5. In a certain school, all the Secondary Three students study at least one of the subjects Physics, Elementary Mathematics and Additional Mathematics. It is given that all the 25 students who study Additional Mathematics also study Elementary Mathematics; 20 students study both Physics and Additional Mathematics; 105 students study Elementary Mathematics and Physics and 40 students study Elementary Mathematics only. Given also that the number of students who study Physics is four-fifth the number of students who study Elementary Mathematics,

(a) illustrate the above information on a Venn diagram,

(b) find the number of students who study Physics only,

(c) find the number of Secondary Three students. [6]

Ans (a)

(b) _____

(c) _____

6. A particle starts from rest and accelerates at 4 m/s² for the first 10 seconds. It continues to accelerate at 2 m/s² for the next 10 seconds and is then uniformly retarded till it comes to rest after a further 10 seconds.

    (a) Draw a sketch of the speed-time graph of the particle for the whole 30 seconds of its motion. [3]

    (b) Calculate the maximum speed of the particle. [2]

    (c) Calculate the retardation during the last 10 seconds. [2]

Ans (a)

(b) _____

(c) _____

7.

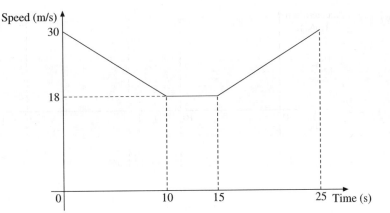

The diagram illustrates the speed of a car during a period of 25 seconds.

(a) Calculate the retardation during the first 10 seconds.   [2]
(b) Calculate the distance travelled during the first 5 seconds.   [2]
(c) Show that the distance travelled during the 25 seconds is 570 m.   [2]
(d) Find the average speed of the car during the 25 seconds.   [2]
(e) On the axes in the answer space, sketch an acceleration-time graph of the car
for the 25 seconds of its journey.   [2]

Ans (a) _____

(b) _____

(d) _____

(e)

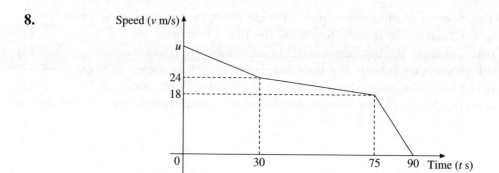

8.

The diagram is the speed-time graph of a train which is brought to rest in three stages over a period of 90 seconds. Calculate

(a) the value of t when $v = 6$, [2]

(b) the value of v when $t = 60$, [2]

(c) the distance travelled in the last 30 seconds, [2]

(d) the value of u, if the distance travelled in the first 30 seconds is 840 m. [2]

Ans *(a)* _____

(b) _____

(c) _____

(d) _____

1. Copy the following figures on graph paper. Draw and label the image of each figure under the transformation as instructed. Give the coordinates of the vertices in each case.

(a)

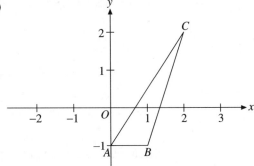

    (i) Reflection in the *x*-axis.
    (ii) Reflection in the line *y* = *x*.

(b)

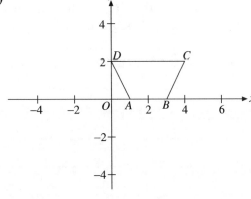

    (i) Anticlockwise rotation of 90° about the origin.
    (ii) 180° rotation about (4, –2).

(c)

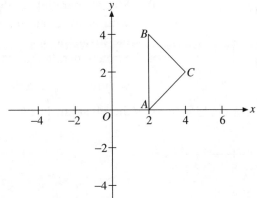

    (i) Enlargement with centre (0, 0) and scale factor $\dfrac{1}{4}$.
    (ii) Enlargement with centre (1, –1) and scale factor –2.

(d)

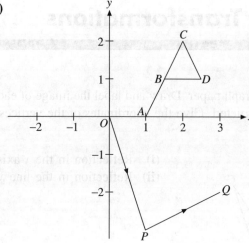

Translation in the direction and distance represented by

(i) $\overrightarrow{OP}$,

(ii) $\overrightarrow{PQ}$.

(e)

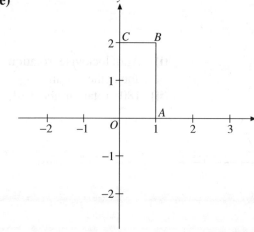

Shear 3 units in the positive direction and having

(i) OA as the invariant line segment,

(ii) OC as the invariant line segment.

(f)

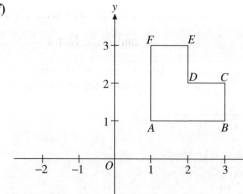

(i) Stretch parallel to the x-axis with factor 2 and the y-axis as the invariant line.

(ii) Stretch parallel to the y-axis with factor $\dfrac{1}{2}$ and the x-axis as the invariant line.

2. Under a translation $\overrightarrow{OP}$, where O is $(0, 0)$ and P is $(3, -2)$, the point $(2, 7)$ is mapped onto the point (a, b), and the image of the point (c, d) is $(-1, -5)$. Find the values of a, b, c and d.

3. Under a translation T, the point $(5, 2)$ is mapped onto the point $(2, 3)$. Find
   (a) the image of the point $(-2, 0)$,
   (b) the point whose image is $(5, -3)$.

4. The vertices of a quadrilateral are $A(3, 0)$, $B(0, -4)$, $C(-1, -3)$ and $D(-2, 3)$. Find the coordinates of the images of A, B, C and D under the transformation given in each case.
   (a) A reflection in (i) the x-axis,
       (ii) the y-axis,
       (iii) the line $x = 1$,
       (iv) the line $y = -2$,
       (v) the line $y = x$,
       (vi) the line $x + y = 3$.
   (b) A rotation of (i) $90°$ clockwise about the origin,
       (ii) $90°$ anticlockwise about the point $(2, 0)$,
       (iii) $180°$ about $(4, -1)$.
   (c) A translation (i) $\overrightarrow{OT}$ where O is $(0, 0)$ and T is $(1, 5)$,
       (ii) $\overrightarrow{PQ}$ where P is $(1, 4)$ and B is $(3, -1)$.
   (d) An enlargement (i) with centre $(0, 0)$ and scale factor $-\dfrac{1}{2}$,
       (ii) with centre $(2, 0)$ and scale factor 3.

5. Give the equations of the images obtained when the following lines are reflected in
   (a) the x-axis,
   (b) the y-axis,
   (c) $y = 1$.

   (i) $x = -\dfrac{1}{2}$ (ii) $y = 3$
   (iii) $x + y = 5$ (iv) $3x - y = 0$

6. What is the equation of the line of reflection for each of the following cases?
   (a) $A(2, 3)$ and $A'(-2, 3)$ (b) $B(-1, 4)$ and $B'(4, -1)$
   (c) $C(0, 4)$ and $C'(-4, 0)$ (d) $D(3, -2)$ and $D'(7, -2)$
   (e) $E(1, 0)$ and $E'(1, -4)$ (f) $F(-3, -4)$ and $F'(4, 3)$

7. Give the equations of the images obtained when the following lines are rotated about the origin.
   (a) $x = 2$, $90°$ clockwise
   (b) $y = -1$, $180°$
   (c) $y = x - 3$, $90°$ anticlockwise

111

8. Give the equations of the images obtained when the following lines are given a translation
    (a)   which maps the point $P(-2, 3)$ onto the point $P'(1, 3)$,
    (b)   which maps the point $Q(2, 6)$ onto the point $Q'(2, 4)$.
          (i) $y = x$
          (ii) $2x + y = 2$

9. (a)   M is a reflection in the line $y = -x$. Find the coordinates of the image of $(3, -1)$ under M.
    (b)   Under a translation T, the point $(4, 1)$ is mapped onto the point $(1, 2)$. Given that T maps $(x, 2)$ onto $(-2, y)$, find the value of x and of y.
    (c)   Write down the coordinates of the image of $P(2, 3)$ under the transformation
          (i) T^2,
          (ii) TM.

10. The square $ABCD$ of side 2 units is mapped onto $ABPQ$ by a shear with AB as the invariant line segment such that D moves 3 units to the right, parallel to AB.
    (a)   Write down the coordinates of B, C, D, P and Q.
    (b)   Find the area of
          (i) $ABPQ$,
          (ii) $\triangle AQD$.

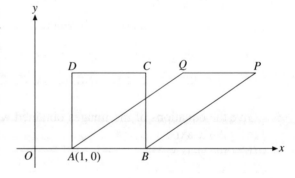

11. Rectangle $ABCD$ is mapped onto $ABPQ$ by a shear and Q is the midpoint of CD.
    (a)   Name the invariant line segment.
    (b)   Find the coordinates of A, C, D and Q.
    (c)   Calculate the area of $ABPQ$.

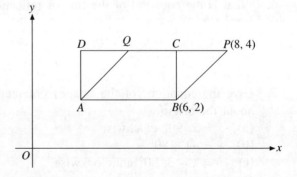

12. △*ABC* is mapped onto △*ABP* by a shear.
   (a) Name the invariant line segment.
   (b) Find the coordinates of *C* if *C* moves 7 units to *P*.
   (c) Find the area of △*ABC*.

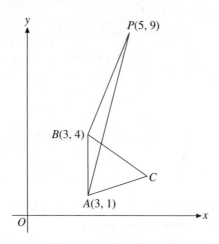

13. (a) △*OAB* is mapped onto △*OA'B* by a shear.
   (i) Name the invariant line segment.
   (ii) If *A* moves 6 units to *A'*, find the coordinates of *A'*.
   (b) △*OAB* is mapped onto △*OAB'* by a transformation H.
   △*OAB* is mapped onto △*AOB'* by a transformation M.
   Describe completely the transformations H and M.
   (c) Find the area of *OAA'B*.
   (d) A shear maps △*OAB'* onto △*OB'C*.
   (i) Name the invariant point.
   (ii) Find the coordinates of *C*.
   (iii) Calculate the area of △*OAC*.

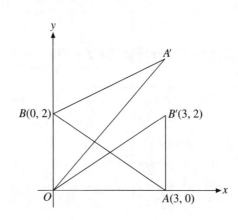

113

14. Find the vertices and the area of the image of △ABC when it is given a stretching
    (a) parallel to the x-axis with factor 3,
    (b) parallel to the y-axis with factor $1\frac{1}{2}$.

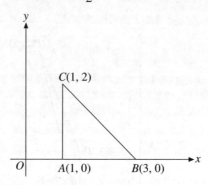

15. The vertices of a triangle are A(5, 0), B(3, 2) and C(6, 5). Find the vertices of its
    image when △ABC is given a stretching
    (a) parallel to the y-axis with factor 2. Name the invariant point.
    (b) with factor $\frac{1}{3}$ and with the y-axis as the invariant line.

16. Describe completely a single transformation which maps △ABC onto
    (a) △LMN,
    (b) △PQR,
    (c) △ADE,
    (d) △XYZ.

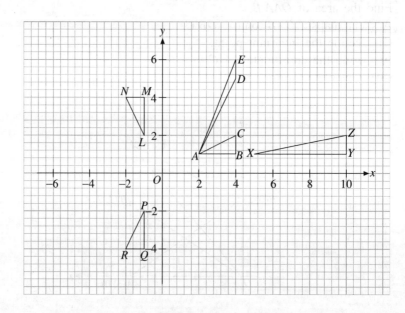

114

17. $\triangle A_1B_1O$ is the image of $\triangle ABO$ under the transformation H.
$\triangle A_2B_2O$ is the image of $\triangle A_1B_1O$ under the transformation M.
Describe H and M completely.

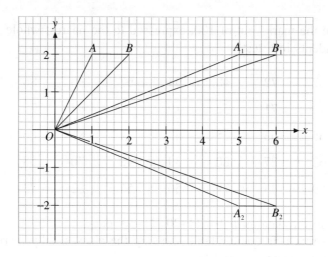

18. (a) Using a scale of 1 cm to represent 1 unit on each axis, draw and label $\triangle ABC$, whose vertices are $A(1, 0)$, $B(4, 2)$ and $C(5, 0)$.

(b) The translation T maps $\triangle ABC$ onto $\triangle A_1B_1C_1$ where A_1 has coordinates $(3, -2)$. Draw and label $\triangle A_1B_1C_1$.

(c) M is a reflection in the y-axis which maps $\triangle ABC$ onto $\triangle A_2B_2C_2$. Draw and label $\triangle A_2B_2C_2$.

(d) The point B is mapped onto the point B_3 by the transformation MT. Mark and label the point B_3.

(e) The shear H maps $\triangle ABC$ onto $\triangle AB_4C$, with AC as the invariant line segment such that B moves 2 units to the right parallel to AC. Draw and label $\triangle AB_4C$.

(f) Find the areas of $\triangle ABC$, $\triangle A_1B_1C_1$, $\triangle A_2B_2C_2$ and $\triangle AB_4C$.

CHAPTER 14 — Statistics

1. Below are the marks out of 100, expressed to the nearest whole number, obtained by 40 students in a test.

87	72	48	93	67	90	86	64
12	71	52	19	77	87	75	52
65	63	55	42	34	81	66	29
63	27	80	39	42	70	58	49
59	44	79	50	51	82	73	78

(a) Group the data as 1–10, 11–20, 21–30, etc.
Construct a frequency table showing the classes, tally marks, midpoints (x), the frequencies (f) and fx.

(b) Represent the grouped data by
(i) a frequency diagram,
(ii) a frequency polygon.

(c) How many students scored more than 70 marks?

(d) Find **(i)** the mean score,
(ii) the modal class,
(iii) the class in which the median lies.

2. The marks scored by 170 students in a test are grouped as follows:

Marks (x)	Frequency
$0 \leqslant x \leqslant 30$	18
$30 < x \leqslant 40$	12
$40 < x \leqslant 60$	48
$60 < x \leqslant 70$	28
$70 < x \leqslant 80$	30
$80 < x \leqslant 100$	34

(a) Construct a histogram for the frequency distribution.
(b) State the modal class.

3. A survey is carried out to find out the number of hours of overtime work claimed by the employees of a certain company. The histogram below illustrates the results of the survey.

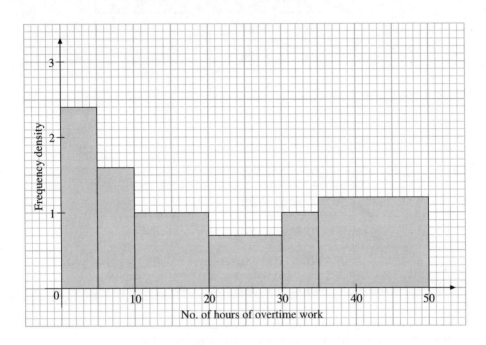

(a) Complete the following table.

No. of hours of overtime work (H)	No. of employees
$0 \leqslant H \leqslant 5$	
$5 < H \leqslant 10$	8
$10 < H \leqslant 20$	
$20 < H \leqslant 30$	7
$30 < H \leqslant 35$	5
$35 < H \leqslant 50$	

(b) How many employees are involved in the survey?

(c) Work out an estimate of the mean number of hours of overtime work.

4. The table shows the frequency distribution of the marks scored by 40 students in a test.

Score (x)	Frequency
$0 < x \leqslant 10$	0
$10 < x \leqslant 20$	2
$20 < x \leqslant 30$	2
$30 < x \leqslant 40$	2
$40 < x \leqslant 50$	6
$50 < x \leqslant 60$	6
$60 < x \leqslant 70$	7
$70 < x \leqslant 80$	8
$80 < x \leqslant 90$	6
$90 < x \leqslant 100$	1

(a) Construct a cumulative frequency table.
(b) Draw a cumulative frequency curve for the data.
(c) Find (i) the lower quartile,
    (ii) the 75th percentile,
    (iii) the median,
    (iv) the interquartile range of the distribution.
(d) If 65% of the students passed the test, what was the passing mark?
(e) How many students scored more than 75 marks?

5. A survey was conducted to find out the number of cars passing a road junction during 35 equal intervals of time. It is found that the highest possible number of cars passing the road junction is 6. The results were recorded in the following table.

No. of cars	0	1	2	3	4	>4
Frequency	7	8	6	4	3	7

Draw a histogram to represent this data.

6. In a contest, 200 students had to mark the names of as many streets as they could on a map of Singapore. The results are given in the following table.

No. of streets correct (x)	46	47	48	49	50	51	52	53
No. of students	13	24	45	47	28	16	17	10

(a) Complete the following cumulative frequency table.

No. of streets correct	46	47	48	49	50	51	52	53
No. of students of this score or less	13						190	200

(b) Draw a cumulative frequency curve for the data.

7. The graph is a cumulative frequency curve showing the daily expenses of 80 students. Use the graph to find, as accurately as possible,
   (a) the median,
   (b) the interquartile range,
   (c) the number of students who spend $2.20 or more,
   (d) the number of students who spend at least $3 but less than $4.50,
   (e) the values of a, b and c in the table below.

Daily Expenses $x	$x < 1$	$1 \leqslant x < 2$	$2 \leqslant x < 3$	$3 \leqslant x < 4$	$4 \leqslant x < 5$
No. of students	0	10	a	b	c

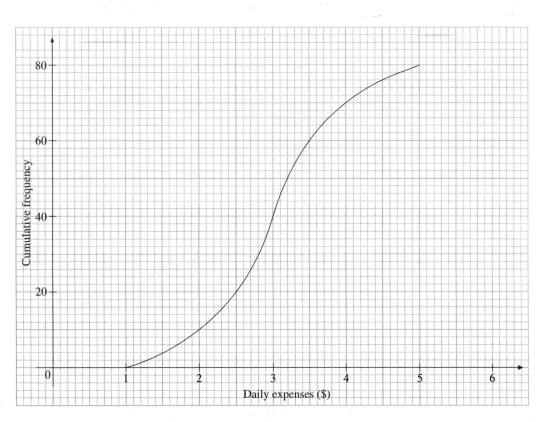

Daily expenses ($)

8. The table below shows the distribution of the speeds, in km/h, of 100 cars.

Speed x km/h	$x \leqslant 50$	$50 < x \leqslant 60$	$60 < x \leqslant 70$	$70 < x \leqslant 80$	$80 < x \leqslant 90$	$90 < x \leqslant 100$
No. of cars	3	6	12	22	42	15

(a) Complete the cumulative frequency table below.

Speed x km/h	50	60	70	80	90	100
No. of cars less than or equal to this speed	3					100

(b) Using a scale of 2 cm to represent 10 km/h on the horizontal axis and 2 cm to represent 10 cars on the vertical axis, draw the cumulative frequency curve.
(c) Use your graph to estimate
    (i) the median speed,
    (ii) the interquartile range,
    (iii) the number of cars with a speed not more than 67 km/h.
(d) A car travelling at a speed exceeding 85 km/h can be charged for speeding. Find the number of cars that are likely to be issued a traffic summon.

TEST PAPER 6

Time : 1 hour
Marks : 50

1. **(a)** Write down the coordinates of *C*, *D* and *Q*. [3]

   (b) Describe completely a single transformation that maps the square *ABCD* onto
   - **(i)** *APQD*,
   - **(ii)** *PBCQ*,
   - **(iii)** *BPQC*,
   - **(iv)** *CBPQ*,
   - **(v)** *ABQC*. [5]

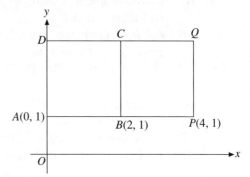

Ans (a)   *C*(,   )

        D(,   )

        Q(,   )

  (b) (i) _____

_____

     (ii) _____

_____

    (iii) _____

_____

    (iv) _____

_____

     (v) _____

_____

2. Answer the whole of this question on a piece of graph paper.

   (a) Using a scale of 1 cm to represent 1 unit on each axis, draw and label $\triangle ABC$ whose vertices are $A(2, 2)$, $B(4, 2)$ and $C(3, 4)$. [3]

   (b) $\triangle ABC$ is mapped onto $\triangle A_1B_1C_1$ by a translation where A_1 has coordinates $(-2, -2)$. Draw and label $\triangle A_1B_1C_1$. [1]

   (c) **(i)** $\triangle ABC$ is mapped onto $\triangle A_1B_2C_2$ by a reflection in the line $y = -x$. Draw and label $\triangle A_1B_2C_2$. [1]

   (ii) $\triangle A_1B_1C_1$ is mapped onto $\triangle A_1B_2C_2$ by a reflection in the line m. Find the equation of the line m. [1]

   (d) $\triangle A_3B_3C_3$ has vertices $(8, -1)$, $(4, 1)$ and $(6, -5)$. Draw and label $\triangle A_3B_3C_3$. [1]

   An enlargement maps $\triangle ABC$ onto $\triangle A_3B_3C_3$.
   (i) Write down the coordinates of the centre of the enlargement. [1]
   (ii) Write down the scale factor of the enlargement. [1]
   (iii) Find the value of the ratio

   $$\frac{\text{area of } \triangle ABC}{\text{area of } \triangle A_3 B_3 C_3}.$$ [1]

   (e) $\triangle ABC$ is mapped onto $\triangle A_4B_4C_4$ by a stretch parallel to the y-axis, with factor $2\frac{1}{2}$. Draw and label $\triangle A_4B_4C_4$. [1]

   (f) $\triangle ABC$ is mapped onto $\triangle ABC_5$ by a shear with AB as the invariant line segment and which moves C 3 units to the right parallel to AB. Draw and label $\triangle ABC_5$. [1]

   (g) $\triangle ABC$ is mapped onto $\triangle A_6B_6C_6$ by an anticlockwise rotation. Given that A_6 is the point $(-2, 2)$,
   (i) draw and label $\triangle A_6B_6C_6$, [1]
   (ii) state the angle and the centre of rotation, [2]
   (iii) describe fully the transformation which maps $\triangle A_6B_6C_6$ onto
     (a) $\triangle A_1B_2C_2$, [1]
     (b) $\triangle B_2A_1C_2$. [1]

   Ans (c) *(ii)* _____

   (d) *(i)* _____

   (ii) _____

   (iii) _____

   (g) *(ii)* _____

   (iii) *(a)* _____

   _____

   (b) _____

   _____

3. The graph is the cumulative frequency curve showing the distance travelled by 50 students from home to school.

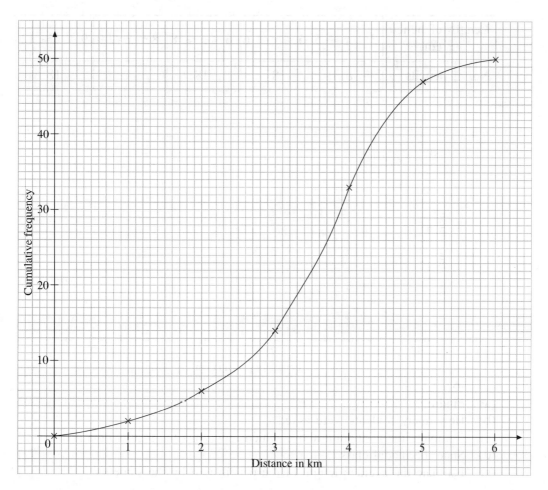

Using the curve, estimate for this group of students,
(a) the median distance travelled from home to school, [1]
(b) the interquartile range of the distribution, [2]
(c) the number of students who travelled at least 3.5 km from home to school, [2]
(d) the values of a, b and c in the table below.

Distance (x) in km	$0 \leqslant x \leqslant 1$	$1 < x \leqslant 2$	$2 < x \leqslant 3$	$3 < x \leqslant 4$	$4 < x \leqslant 5$	$5 < x \leqslant 6$
No. of students	2	a	8	19	b	c

[3]

Ans (a) _____ *(b)* _____

(c) _____ *(d)* _____

123

4. A group of students were asked to measure the length of the pencil they are using. The results are shown in the following table and histogram.

Length of pencil (x cm)	$3 < x \leqslant 5$	$5 < x \leqslant 6$	$6 < x \leqslant 8$	$8 < x \leqslant 9$	$9 < x \leqslant 12$
No. of pencils	a	8	18	4	18

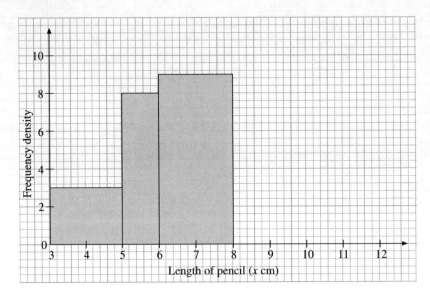

(a)   Find a.   [1]
(b)   How many students were asked?   [1]
(c)   Complete the histogram above which represents the results obtained.   [2]
(d)   State the modal class.   [1]
(e)   Estimate the average length of the pencil used by the students.   [2]

Ans (a) _____

(b) _____

(d) _____

(e) _____

5. The ages of 80 elderly people in a nursing home are given in the table below.

Age in years (x)	$60 \leqslant x < 65$	$65 \leqslant x < 70$	$70 \leqslant x < 80$	$80 \leqslant x < 90$	$90 \leqslant x < 100$
No. of people	21	17	24	12	6

(a) In a histogram, the height of the column representing $65 \leqslant x < 70$ was 6.8 cm. Calculate the height of the column representing $80 \leqslant x < 90$. [2]

Ans _____

(b) Complete the following cumulative frequency table. [2]

Age in years	< 60	< 65	< 70	< 80	< 90	< 100
No. of people	0	21				80

(c) Using a horizontal scale of 2 cm to represent 5 years and a vertical scale of 2 cm to represent 10 people, draw a cumulative frequency curve to illustrate this distribution. [2]

(d) Use your curve to estimate the following:
    (i) The median age of the group [1]
    (ii) The interquartile range [2]
    (iii) The number of elderly people who are at least 85 years old [1]

Ans (d) (i) _____

(ii) _____

(iii) _____

FINAL TERM ASSESSMENT

Time : $1\frac{1}{2}$ hours

Marks: 52

Section I

Answer **ALL** questions in this section.
All working must be clearly shown in the space provided.
Calculators are **NOT** allowed in this section.

1. Evaluate the following, giving your answer in the standard form.
    (a) Cube of 0.008   [2]
    (b) Reciprocal of 0.008   [2]

Ans (a) _____

(b) _____

2. Find the value of
    (a) $\sqrt{48\,900}$,   [2]
    (b) $\sqrt{0.489}$.   [2]
    [$\sqrt{4.89} = 2.211, \sqrt{48.9} = 6.993$]

Ans (a) _____

(b) _____

3. Simplify $\dfrac{a^2 - b^2}{a^3 - a^2 b}$. Hence, evaluate $\dfrac{a^2 - b^2}{a^3 - a^2 b}$ when $a = 2$ and $b = \dfrac{2}{3}$. [4]

Ans _____

_____

4. In $\triangle ABC$, $AB = 7$ cm, $BC = 10$ cm and $AC = 8$ cm. If θ is the smallest angle in the triangle, calculate $\cos \theta$, giving your answer as a fraction in its simplest form.
[4]

Ans _____

5. Given that $5 \leqslant x \leqslant 10$, $y = \dfrac{k}{x^3}$, where k is a constant and the smallest value of y is 2, find

    (a) the value of k,   [2]

    (b) the largest value of y,   [2]

    (c) the largest value of $\dfrac{x - y}{xy}$.   [2]

Ans (a) _____

(b) _____

(c) _____

6. The diagram is a sketch of the curve $y = (3 - x)(2 + x)$. Write down

    (a) the coordinates of A, B and C,   [2]

    (b) the equation of the line of symmetry,   [1]

    (c) the range of values of x for which $(3 - x)(2 + x) < 0$.   [1]

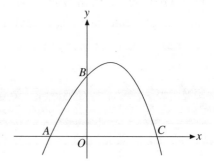

Ans (a) _____

(b) _____

(c) _____

7.

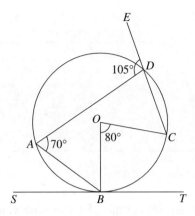

In the diagram, O is the centre of the circle and ST is a tangent to the circle at B. $B\hat{O}C = 80°$, $B\hat{A}D = 70°$ and $A\hat{D}E = 105°$. Calculate

(a) $O\hat{B}C$, [2]

(b) $O\hat{C}D$, [2]

(c) $C\hat{B}T$, [2]

(d) $S\hat{B}A$. [2]

Ans (a) _____

(b) _____

(c) _____

(d) _____

129

8.

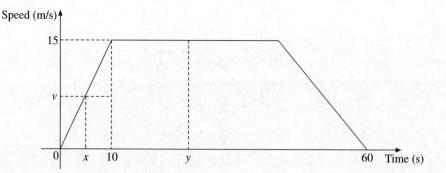

The diagram is the speed-time graph of a van. The van starts from rest and steadily accelerates to a speed of 15 m/s in 10 seconds. Its speed then remains constant for some time before it steadily decelerates at $\dfrac{3}{4}$ m/s² until it stops. The whole journey takes one minute.

(a) For how long does the van travel at the maximum speed?   [2]
(b) Given that the speed after x s is v m/s, express v in terms of x.   [1]
(c) Given that the distance travelled during the period from $t = 0$ to $t = y$ is d m, express d in terms of y.   [2]
(d) Convert the speed of 15 m/s into km/h.   [1]

Ans (a) _____

(b) _____

(c) _____

(d) _____

9. An isosceles triangle, △*ABC*, is mapped onto △*AB'C'* by a shear and *M* is the midpoint of *AB*.

    (a) Name the invariant point.   [1]

    (b) Find the coordinates of *C*, *B'* and *M'*, the image of *M*.   [3]

    (c) Calculate the area of △*ACC'*.   [2]

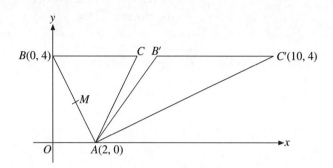

Ans (a) _____

(b) _____

(c) _____

131

10. (a)

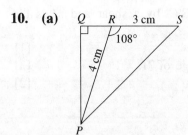

In $\triangle PQS$, $P\hat{Q}S = 90°$, $P\hat{R}S = 108°$, $RS = 3$ cm and $PR = 4$ cm.
Calculate
(i) the area of $\triangle PRS$, [2]
(ii) the length of QR. [1]
[Given $\sin 72° = 0.951$, $\cos 72° = 0.309$ and $\tan 72° = 3.078$]

Ans (i) _____

(ii) _____

(b)

North

B

A

71°

122°

27°

D

C

In the figure, $C\hat{A}D = 71°$, $A\hat{B}C = 122°$ and $A\hat{C}B = 27°$. Find the bearing of
(i) B from A,
(ii) A from C,
(iii) C from B. [3]

Ans (i) _____

(ii) _____

(iii) _____

Time : 1 hour

Marks : 48

Section II

Answer any **FOUR** questions.
Each question carries 12 marks.
Calculators may be used in this section.

1. **(a)** In the Venn diagram, shade
   (i) $(A \cup B) \cap C$,   **(ii)** $(A \cap B) \cup (B \cap C)$,

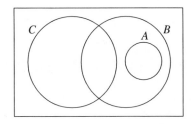   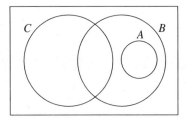

   (iii) $(A' \cap B) \cap C'$.

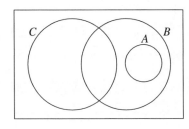

[3]

   (b) $\mathcal{E}$ = {letters of the word ARCHIPELAGO}
   A = {letters of the word CHEAP}
   B = {letters of the word LARGE}
   C = {letters of the word PALACE}
   (i) State the value of n$(A \cap B)$.
   (ii) Simplify $(A \cup B) \cap$ C.   [2]

   Ans (b) (i) _____

   (ii) _____

(c) 50 people were asked whether they patronised any of the 3 fast food outlets – Burger-A, Burger-B and Burger-C, in a particular month.

Of the 25 people who patronised Burger-A,
  x also went to Burger-B and Burger-C,
  5 went to Burger-B but not Burger-C,
  9 did not go to Burger-B and Burger-C.

Of the 25 people who did not go to Burger-A,
  $x + 1$ went to Burger-B and Burger-C,
  $2x$ went only to Burger C,
  9 went only to Burger-B.

On the Venn diagram, show the number of people in each subset. Hence, find
(i) the value of x,
(ii) the number of people who went to at least 2 of the fast food outlets,
(iii) the percentage of people who patronised Burger-C. [7]

Ans

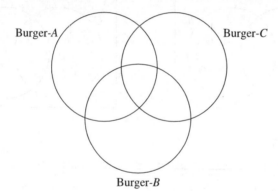

(c) (i) _____

(ii) _____

(iii) _____

2. (a) The diagram shows a pyramid with a rectangular base *ABCD* and vertex *V* vertically above *C*.
Find **(i)** the angle of elevation of *V* from *A*, [2]

  (ii) the size of $B\hat{V}D$. [3]

Give your answers correct to one decimal place.

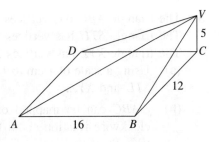

Ans (i) _____

(ii) _____

(b) *P, Q, R* and *S* are four points on level ground. *Q, R* and *S* lie on a straight line. The bearing of *R* from *P* is 060°, the bearing of *Q* from *R* is 124° and *Q* is due east of *P*.
Given that *PR = RS* = 10 km, calculate, to 1 decimal place,

(i)   the distance *PQ*, [3]
(ii)   the distance *PS*, [2]
(iii) the bearing of *S* from *P*. [2]

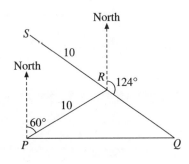

Ans (i) _____

(ii) _____

(iii) _____

3. The triangle ABC has vertices $A(8, -2)$, $B(4, 0)$ and $C(7, -4)$.
   The triangle STU has vertices $S(2, 0)$, $T(4, 4)$ and $U(0, 1)$.
   The triangle XYZ has vertices $X(2, -6)$, $Y(0, -2)$ and $Z(4, -5)$.
   (a) Using a scale of 1 cm to 1 unit on each axis, draw and label the triangles ABC,
       STU and XYZ. [3]
   (b) $\triangle ABC$ can be mapped onto $\triangle STU$ under a translation $\overrightarrow{OP}$, followed by a
       clockwise rotation about the origin.
       (i) State the angle of rotation.
       (ii) Write down the coordinates of P.
       (iii) Describe completely a single transformation which maps $\triangle ABC$ onto
             $\triangle STU$. [3]

                                          Ans (b) (i) _____

                                               (ii) _____

                                              (iii) _____

   (c) Given that $\triangle ABC$ can be mapped onto $\triangle XYZ$ by a translation $\overrightarrow{OQ}$, where
       $Q = (-2, 0)$, followed by a reflection in the line l. Draw the line l on your
       graph and write down its equation. [2]

   (d) $\triangle A_1B_1C_1$ is the image of $\triangle ABC$ under an enlargement with scale factor $-\dfrac{1}{2}$
       and centre $(0, 0)$. Draw and label $\triangle A_1B_1C_1$. [2]

   (e) $\triangle A_2B_1C_2$ is the image of $\triangle A_1B_1C_1$ under a stretch parallel to the y-axis with
       factor 4. Draw and label $\triangle A_2B_1C_2$. [2]

4. **(a)** $\mathcal{E} = \{x : x$ is an integer, $3 \leqslant x \leqslant 10\}$
$A = \{x : x^3 < 400\}$
$B = \{x : 13 < 4x < 38\}$
List the elements of
  (i) A,
  (ii) B',
  (iii) $A' \cap B$,
  (iv) $A' \cup B'$. [4]

Ans (i) _____

  (ii) _____

  (iii) _____

  (iv) _____

(b) The area of a rectangle $ABCD$ is 20 cm^2. P is a point on AB such that $BP = 2$ cm and R is a point on AD such that $DR = 1$ cm. The rectangle $APQR$ is drawn inside $ABCD$.

    (i)   Taking AP to be x cm, write down the expressions for the lengths of AB and AR.   [2]

Ans (i) _____

_____

    (ii)   Given that the area of $APQR$ is 6 cm^2, form an equation in x and show that it reduces to $x^2 - 12x + 12 = 0$.   [3]

    (iii)   Solve the equation $x^2 - 12x + 12 = 0$ and hence, find the two possible lengths of AD, giving your answers correct to 2 decimal places.   [3]

Ans (iii) _____

5. (a) The following table gives the frequency distribution of marks obtained by 150 candidates in an examination.

Marks	No. of candidates
$0 \leqslant x \leqslant 10$	2
$10 < x \leqslant 20$	6
$20 < x \leqslant 30$	9
$30 < x \leqslant 40$	7
$40 < x \leqslant 50$	20
$50 < x \leqslant 60$	32
$60 < x \leqslant 70$	30
$70 < x \leqslant 80$	24
$80 < x \leqslant 90$	14
$90 < x \leqslant 100$	6

(i) Construct a cumulative frequency table for classes '10 marks or less', '20 marks or less' and so on. [2]

(ii) Using a scale of 1 cm to represent 10 marks on the horizontal axis and 1 cm to represent 10 candidates on the vertical axis, draw the cumulative frequency curve for the distribution. [2]

(iii) Use your graph to estimate

    (a) the median mark, [1]

    (b) the interquartile range, [2]

    (c) the number of candidates who will obtain a distinction if the minimum mark for a distinction is 84. [1]

Ans (i)

(iii) (a) _____

(b) _____

(c) _____

(b) The table below shows the weight of 40 students.

Weight (w) in kg	$40 < w \leqslant 50$	$50 < w \leqslant 60$	$60 < w \leqslant 65$	$65 < w \leqslant 70$
Frequency	6	8	12	14

    (i)   Construct a histogram to illustrate this distribution.   [3]
    (ii) State the modal class.   [1]

Ans (ii) _____

ANSWERS

Chapter 1

1. (a) 81   (b) $\dfrac{1}{343}$ (c) $\dfrac{8}{125}$ (d) 16

(e) $\dfrac{27}{343}$ (f) 625   (g) $\dfrac{3}{8}$ (h) 4

(i) 1 331   (j) 81   (k) $\dfrac{1}{3}$ (l) 2

(m) 0.6   (n) $\dfrac{1}{27}$

2. (a) 9   (b) $\dfrac{9}{4}$ (c) $\dfrac{8}{27}$ (d) $\dfrac{125}{27}$

(e) 36   (f) $\dfrac{1}{4}$ (g) -25 (h) $-\dfrac{1}{2}$

(i) 8   (j) $\dfrac{1}{4}$ (k) -0.7 (l) 0.64

(m) $\dfrac{11}{9}$ (n) 1 000

3. (a) 81   (b) 2   (c) 1   (d) $\dfrac{1}{729}$

(e) $\dfrac{1}{16}$ (f) $\dfrac{1}{27}$ (g) $\dfrac{1}{4}$ (h) 0

(i) 4   (j) 2   (k) 5   (l) 5

(m) 64   (n) 4   (o) $\dfrac{1}{8}$ (p) $\dfrac{1}{125}$

(q) 81   (r) 3   (s) 9   (t) $\dfrac{1}{625}$

4. (a) 6   (b) 125   (c) 49   (d) $\dfrac{1}{27}$

(e) $\dfrac{1}{4}$ (f) 9   (g) $\dfrac{1}{9}$ (h) $\dfrac{3}{7}$

(i) 40   (j) 1   (k) 1   (l) 20

(m) 216   (n) $\dfrac{1}{11}$ (o) $\dfrac{5}{9}$ (p) 16

(q) $\dfrac{400}{9}$ (r) 1   (s) 2   (t) $\dfrac{1}{9}$

5. (a) $72a^{\frac{5}{6}}$ (b) $a^{-\frac{4}{3}}$ (c) $x^{\frac{5}{4}}y^{\frac{9}{14}}$ (d) $\left(\dfrac{b}{a}\right)^{\frac{3}{2}}$

(e) xy^{-4} (f) $\dfrac{-y^{10}}{x^{6}}$ (g) $\dfrac{b^{3}}{a^{24}}$ (h) $a^{-\frac{6}{5}}$

6. (a) $2a^6$ (b) a^6 (c) $3x^8y$ (d) $\dfrac{5}{2}p^3q^5r^{\frac{8}{3}}$

(e) $(a+2b)^{\frac{5}{2}}$ (f) $x^{-\frac{5}{6}}$ (g) $m^2n^{\frac{7}{12}}$ (h) $a^3b^{\frac{5}{2}}$

(i) $a^{\frac{1}{6}}$ (j) $\dfrac{3}{p^{\frac{1}{8}}}$ (k) $6p$

7. (a) 64 (b) $\dfrac{16}{81}$ (c) $\dfrac{1}{25}$ (d) 4

(e) $\dfrac{1}{128}$ (f) 1 (g) 243 (h) $\dfrac{1}{64}$

(i) $50\ 000$ (j) $6\dfrac{1}{16}$ (k) $4\dfrac{2}{3}$

8. (a) $\dfrac{1}{3}$ (b) $-\dfrac{1}{2}$ (c) $-\dfrac{1}{6}$ (d) $3\dfrac{1}{2}$

(e) $-2\dfrac{1}{2}$ (f) 5 (g) $\dfrac{1}{2}$ (h) -1 or 2

(i) $x=\dfrac{4}{5},\ y=\dfrac{11}{10}$ (j) $x=-1,\ y=1$

9. (a) $x=a^{\frac{n}{m}}$ (b) 2
10. (a) $2x-7$ (b) $-8x^2-28x$
11. (a) $8x+9$ (b) $9-4x^2$
12. (a) $-5a-b$ (b) $4b+6a^2-15ab$
13. $12x^2y^3-15x^3y^2$ **14.** $2-18x^2$
15. $15x^3-2x^2-13x+4$ **16.** $x^5-2x^4+2x^3+9x^2-18x+20$
17. $4x^2+8x-50$ **18.** $32x^2-112x+98$
19. $12x^2+18x-36xy-27y+27y^2$ **20.** $8x^3-36x^2+54x-27$
21. x^4-8x^2+16 **22.** $4x^4+20x^3+13x^2-30x+9$
23. $2x+23$ **24.** $8xy$ **25.** 0 **26.** $9a-5b-c$
27. $-x+3y$ **28.** $-2xz^3$ **29.** $2a^3-4a$ **30.** $3x(1+4x^2)$
31. $(2+a)^2(2-a)$ **32.** $4(xy+5)(xy-5)$ **33.** $2u^2(1+5u)(1-5u)$
34. $(13x+8)(x-3)$ **35.** $3(2y+5x)(y-2x)$ **36.** $(4-3x)(2x-1)$
37. $3(a-2b)(3-a+2b)$ **38.** $(p-2x)(3x-4y)$ **39.** $-5(x+y)(7x+y)$
40. $2a^3bc(1-6ab^2)(1+2ab^2)$ **41.** $(n-4)(m+1)^2$ **42.** $\dfrac{m^2}{3np}$

43. $\dfrac{4x^2y}{3}$ **44.** $\dfrac{y}{3x}$ **45.** $\dfrac{2}{3a(a-2b)}$ **46.** $\dfrac{a^2b}{3}$

47. q^2 **48.** $\dfrac{1}{y^2}$ **49.** $\dfrac{xz^n}{y}$ **50.** $\dfrac{5a^2}{6b^{n+1}}$

51. $\dfrac{21a^{n-3}}{4}$ **52.** $\dfrac{3b+2a}{6a^2}$ **53.** $\dfrac{2x}{y}$ **54.** $\dfrac{x^2+y^2}{(x+y)(x-y)}$

55. $\dfrac{m-n}{m+n}$ **56.** $\dfrac{4}{49}$ **57.** $\dfrac{q}{p-q}$ **58.** $\dfrac{p-1}{p-6}$

59. $-\dfrac{4}{u}$ **60.** $\dfrac{a^2b^2}{3b-a}$ **61.** $\dfrac{(c+5)(c+2)}{2c(5-c)}$ **62.** $-\dfrac{x+y}{y}$

63. $\dfrac{3a}{4a-3}$ **64.** $\dfrac{1}{2}$ **65.** $\dfrac{2}{x-2}$ **66.** $\dfrac{2}{x+2}$

67. $\dfrac{2}{x(2x+1)}$ **68.** $\dfrac{x^2+3x-2}{(x+2)(x-5)}$ **69.** $-\dfrac{1}{2(x+2)}$ **70.** $\dfrac{-2x}{x+3}$

71. $-\dfrac{1}{6m}$ **72.** $\dfrac{3}{x+1}$ **73.** $\dfrac{4}{x(x+6)}$

74. (a) $\dfrac{a-b}{a+b}$ (b) 0.093 0   **75.** (a) $\dfrac{8}{3}$ (b) $-\dfrac{1}{4}$

76. $\dfrac{5}{9}$ **77.** $\dfrac{x-3y}{x}$; $\dfrac{1}{4}$ **78.** (a) 3.06   (b) 0.29

79. (a) 37   (b) 0.55   **80.** 6   **81.** $1\dfrac{2}{3}$

Chapter 2
1. 0.019 1   **2.** −0.027 8   **3.** (a) ±22.4   (b) ±30.9
4. (a) 22.6   (b) 0.230   **5.** (a) 0.004 81   (b) 0.154
6. (a) 1 890 or 1 480   (b) ±1.39   **7.** 1.22

8. 1.64 or 0.243   **9.** −0.139   **10.** $x = \dfrac{w^2+y}{wy}$

11. $x = \dfrac{b(a^2+1)}{a(b^2+1)}$ **12.** $x = \sqrt{\dfrac{b}{c(ab-1)}}$ **13.** $x = \dfrac{pr+1}{2p}$

14. $x = \dfrac{A}{y}$ **15.** $x = \sqrt{\dfrac{p^2T^2}{p^2-T^2}}$ **16.** $x = \dfrac{p^2-1}{2p^2}$

17. (a) $x = -1\dfrac{3}{4}$ (b) $x = 3.90$ or -0.898

18. (a) $y = \pm 2.92$ (b) $y = 0$ or 8.5 (c) $y = 7.34$ or 1.16

19. (a) $x = 0$ or $1\dfrac{1}{2}$ (b) $x = \dfrac{1}{2}$ or 1 (c) $x = 1.90$ or -0.396

20. (a) $x = \dfrac{1}{3}$ or $-\dfrac{1}{3}$ (b) $x = \pm 1.05$ (c) $x = 1\dfrac{1}{3}$ or $-\dfrac{2}{3}$
    (d) $x = 1.07$ or -3.74

21. (a) $y = 2$ (b) $y = 18$ or 24 (c) $y = 1.86$ or -11.9
    (d) $y = 41.3$ or 10.7

22. (a) $x = \dfrac{1}{7}$ (b) $x = 0.549$ or -1.22 (c) $x = \dfrac{2}{3}$ or -1

23. −3.53 or −0.47   **24.** 1.39 or 0.36   **25.** 0.28 or −1.17
26. 5.41 or −2.41   **27.** −0.17 or −1.50   **28.** 1.42 or 0.70
29. −0.52 or −2.15   **30.** 1.59 or 0.16   **31.** 3.15 or 0.85

32. 1.54 or −0.87   **33.** 1.24 or −7.24   **34.** 0.41 or −7.41

35. 2.53 or −1.78   **36.** 4.71 or 3.29   **37.** 3.69 or −1.36

38. 3 or −5   **39.** 4.89 or 0.61   **40.** 1.93 or 0.57

41. 0.88 or −2.28   **42.** 2.85 or −0.35   **43.** 5.65 or −22.65

44. (a) (i) $\dfrac{432}{x}$ (ii) $\dfrac{864}{2x - 21}$

    (c) $x = -13.5$ or 24; 18 min   **45.** 2.10

46. $k = -2$ or 4   **47.** 2.59 or −0.26; 104 mm

48. (a) $\dfrac{1\,400 + 30x}{x}$ (c) (i) $20   (ii) 50 vases

49. $x = 1.11$ or −1.36; 4.89 cm^2

50. (b) 56.0 or −59.0   (c) 3 h 56 min

51. (a) $x = \dfrac{8}{3}$ or −5 (rejected)

    (b) $x = 5.56$ or 4.96 (rejected), perimeter = 40.2 cm

52. $x = 18$ or $-\dfrac{45}{22}$ (rejected); 24 min

53. (a) (i) $\dfrac{40}{x}$ (ii) $\dfrac{40}{x + 5}$ (c) 34.1 l (d) $1.023

Test Paper 1

1. (a) $\dfrac{1}{8}$ (b) 81   (c) $\dfrac{5}{2}$

2. (a) $(ab)^{\frac{1}{2}}$ (b) $\dfrac{1}{2}p^3$

3. (a) $x^3 - 2x^2y - 4xy^2 + 8y^3$ (b) $12bc$

4. (a) $2(7 - x)(1 + 2x)$ (b) $(2 + b)(2 - b)(1 + a)(1 - a)$

5. (a) $\dfrac{a}{a - b}$ (b) $1\dfrac{3}{4}$ **6.** (a) $\dfrac{1}{x}$ (b) $\dfrac{6 - x^2}{x(x - 1)(x + 2)}$

7. (a) $x = \sqrt{\dfrac{b(a^2 - c^2)}{a}}$ (b) $x = \sqrt{\dfrac{2mn}{n^2 - m^2}}$

8. (a) 2.52 or −0.27   (b) 1.35 or −1.85   **9.** $x = 52.7$

10. (a) $(2x - 1)(4x - 7)$ (c) 3.19 or −0.94; 9.95 cm

Chapter 3

1. (a) $x < -\dfrac{7}{2}$ (b) $x \leqslant -6$ (c) $x > \dfrac{11}{4}$

    (d) $-4 < x \leqslant 1$ (e) $\dfrac{3}{5} < x < 2$

2. $k = 34, 35, 36, 37$ **3.** $x = 13$

4. (a) −5, −4, −3   (b) 3   (c) 5, 6, 7   (d) 4, 5

5. (a) −34   (b) 25   (c) −22 and 22   (d) 29

6. (a) 1   (b) −2   (c) $-2\dfrac{3}{5}$

7. (a) (i) $\dfrac{2}{3}$ **(ii)** 74   **(b) (i)** –25   **(ii)** $-\dfrac{17}{3}$

8. (a) 25   **(b)** 1   **(c)** $3\dfrac{3}{4}$

9. (a) –14   **(b)** $\dfrac{8}{7}$ **(c)** $\dfrac{16}{5}$ **(d)** 49

10. $x = 6, 7$ and 8   **(a)** $p = 7$ and $q = 8$ **(b)** $p = 6$ and $q = 7$
    (c) $p = 8$ and $q = 6$ **(d)** $p = 6$ and $q = 8$

11. (a) 195 g and 205 g   **(b)** 158.5 cm and 159.5 cm
    (c) 2.335 l and 2.345 l **(d)** 4.75 km and 4.85 km

12. 12.852 5 cm^2, 14.6 cm

13. (a) 14 cm and 16 cm   **(b)** 144 cm^3 and 146 cm^3
    (c) 3 390 kg and 3 410 kg

14. (a) 17.5 cm and 20.5 cm   **(b)** 17.05 cm and 19.15 cm

15. 198 l and 207 l **16. (a)** 132.25 cm^2 **(b)** 42 cm

17. (a) 200.5 g   **(b)** 5.08 g/cm^3 **(c)** 632 g

18. (a) 4.35 g and 4.45 g   **(b)** 5.24 cm^3 and 4.58 cm^3

19. (a) 14.5 kg   **(b)** 74 cm   **20.** 1 296.75 m

21. 14.25 m and 19.35 m   **22. (a)** $4\dfrac{5}{18}$ cm   **(b)** $3\dfrac{59}{72}$ cm^2

23. (a) 158 cm^3 **(b)** 62 cm^3 **24.** $0 < x < 20$

25. 11 triangles, 8 cm or 6 cm   **26.** 5, 6, 7, 8, 10, 12, 14, 16 sq. units

27. (c, p) : (4, 6), (4, 7), (4, 8), (5, 6), (5, 7), (6, 6)

28. 14   **29.** 57   **30.** 5.4 kg   **31.** 16, 64

32. $5 \leqslant x \leqslant 24$ **33.** $x \geqslant 9$ **34.** 10

35. 12, 14, 16; 14, 16, 18; 16, 18, 20; 18, 20, 22

36. $0 < x < 14$, where x is an integer   **37. (a)** $x > 6$ **(b)** 7

38. 29   **39.** $x < 14$ **40.** More than 9 sweets

Chapter 4

1. (a) $\left(4, \dfrac{1}{2}\right)$, 5, $\dfrac{3}{4}$ **(b)** $\left(\dfrac{5}{2}, 12\right)$, 13, $-\dfrac{12}{5}$ **(c)** $\left(2, -4\dfrac{1}{4}\right)$, $\dfrac{5}{2}$, $\dfrac{3}{4}$

    (d) $\left(-3, \dfrac{1}{9}\right)$, $\dfrac{10}{3}$, $-\dfrac{3}{4}$ **(e)** (4, 4), $2\sqrt{2}$, –1   **(f)** (–4, 0), 10, $-\dfrac{3}{4}$

    (g) $\left(\dfrac{1}{2}, 5\right)$, 5, 0   **(h)** (4, 10), 6, undefined

    (i) $\left(2\dfrac{3}{4}, 7\dfrac{1}{4}\right)$, $\dfrac{1}{2}\sqrt{106}$, $\dfrac{9}{5}$ **(j)** $\left(-\dfrac{5}{2}, 3\right)$, $\sqrt{17}$, 4

    (k) $\left(\dfrac{a + p}{2}, \dfrac{b + q}{2}\right)$, $\sqrt{(a - p)^2 + (b - q)^2}$, $\dfrac{b - q}{a - p}$

    (l) (5p, 5p), 10p, $\dfrac{4}{3}$ **(m)** $\left(\dfrac{9p^2}{2}, \dfrac{7q}{2}\right)$, $3\sqrt{p^4 + q^2}$, $\dfrac{q}{p^2}$

2. (a) $p = -5$ or 11 (b) $p = 4\frac{1}{2}$ (c) $p = -3$

3. (a) 21.86 units, isosceles triangle   (b) 17.41 units

4. (a) $\left(-\frac{1}{2}, 0\right)$ (b) $(-3, 0)$ (c) 10 sq. units   5. $a = \frac{9}{4}$ or $\frac{3}{4}$

6. (a) 34 sq. units   (b) 12 sq. units   7. $t = -9\frac{1}{2}$, $S(5, -1)$

8. (a) $a = 1$, $b = 10$ (b) $a = 2$, $b = 2$ (c) $a = 1$, $b = -1$

9. (a) -1, $\frac{4}{3}$ (b) $\frac{4}{5}$, $\frac{7}{5}$ (c) $\frac{3}{2}$, -6 (d) -4, -12

   (e) undefined, 0   (f) 8, $\frac{2}{3}$ (g) $-\frac{4}{9}$, 0 (h) 0, $-\frac{4}{9}$

   (i) undefined, 0   (j) $-\frac{4}{9}$, 1

10. (i) line g (ii) line f (iii) line d (iv) line a
     (v) line c (vi) line b (vii) line e

11. (i) line h (ii) line c (iii) line a (iv) x-axis
     (v) line e (vi) line g (vii) line d (viii) line f
     (ix) y-axis   (x) line b (xi) line j (xii) line i

12. (a) (i) $(12, 19)$ (ii) 12 units   (b) (i) $(-3, 0)$ (ii) 3 units
    (c) (i) $(0, 5)$ (ii) 0 units   (d) (i) $(3, 7)$ (ii) 15 units

    (e) (i) $(2, 5)$ (ii) undefined   (f) (i) $(-2, 3)$ (ii) $6\frac{1}{5}$ units

13. $A(4, 4)$, $B(0, 5)$, $C(0, 2)$, $D(1, 0)$

14. (a) 0   (b) $6\frac{1}{2}$ (c) $1\frac{2}{3}$

15. (a) -11 (b) 6   (c) -1 or $2\frac{1}{3}$ 16. $\left(-\frac{2}{3}, -5\right)$

17. (a) $\left(\frac{2}{3}, 0\right)$ and $(0, -2)$ (b) $\frac{2}{3}$ sq. units

18. (a) $m = -\frac{1}{2}$, $c = 2$ (b) $m = -1$, $c = 4$

19. (a) $y = \frac{1}{2}x - \frac{2}{3}$ (b) (i) $y = -\frac{3}{2}x - 1$ (ii) $y = -\frac{3}{2}x + \frac{23}{2}$

    (c) $y = \frac{3}{2}x + 2$ (d) (i) $y = 4x$ (ii) $y = 4x - 3$

    (e) (i) $y = -\frac{1}{2}x + 5$ (ii) $y = -7$ (iii) $x = 2\frac{1}{2}$

       (iv) $y = \frac{7}{5}x + 7$ (v) $y = -\frac{5}{4}x$

20. (a) $A\left(4\frac{1}{2}, 0\right)$, $B\left(0, 4\frac{1}{2}\right)$ (b) 15.36 units   (c) Yes, $y = x$

21. (a) $t = 3$ (b) $AD = BC = \sqrt{58}$ (c) isosceles trapezium

(d) Yes, $y = x + 2$ $\qquad$ **(e)** 70 sq. units $\qquad$ **(f)** $P\left(1\frac{5}{7}, 3\frac{5}{7}\right)$

22. (a) gradient $AB = 3$, gradient $PQ = -3$; $AB \not\parallel PQ$

$\qquad$ **(b)** gradient $AB = -\frac{1}{4}$, gradient $PQ = -\frac{1}{4}$; $AB \parallel PQ$

23. (a) $y = \frac{1}{3}x + 3$ $\qquad$ **(b)** $y = -\frac{3}{4}x + \frac{35}{4}$ $\qquad$ **(c)** $y = -\frac{2}{3}x + \frac{5}{3}$

24. (a) and (c) – The lines do not intersect because they have the same gradient, and therefore they are parallel lines.

$\qquad$ **(b)** $(-33, 49)$ $\qquad$ **(d)** $\left(\dfrac{abc}{b^2 - a^2}, \dfrac{a^2c}{a^2 - b^2}\right)$ $\qquad$ **(e)** $\left(-\dfrac{bc}{2a}, \dfrac{c}{2}\right)$

25. (a) $y = -\frac{2}{3}x + 2$ $\qquad$ **(b)** $y = -\frac{2}{3}x - 2$

26. (a) 0 $\qquad$ **(b)** 3 $\qquad$ **(c)** -6

27. (a) $-\frac{4}{3}$ $\qquad$ **(b)** 6 $\qquad$ **(c)** 1 $\qquad$ **(d)** $-\frac{5}{6}$

28. $a = -1$, $b = 10$ $\qquad$ **29. (a)** $\left(1\frac{2}{3}, 0\right)$ $\qquad$ **(b)** $(0, -5)$

30. (a) 2, -3 $\qquad$ **(b)** $-\frac{5}{7}, 3\frac{2}{7}$

Test Paper 2

1. (a) $x < -\frac{5}{6}$ $\qquad$ **(b)** $-2, -1, 0, 1, 2, 3$

2. (a) 6.00 or 0.33 $\qquad$ **(b)** -1 or $3\frac{2}{3}$

3. (a) 19 $\qquad$ **(b)** 25

4. (a) 9.8 s $\qquad$ **(b)** 510 ml and 550 ml

5. (a) (i) $\$(7 - x)$ **(ii)** $\dfrac{36}{7 - x}$ $\qquad$ **(b)** $\dfrac{36}{7 - x} - \dfrac{36}{x} = 3$; $x = 4$ or -21; \$4

6. (a) (i) $x = 4$, $y = -1$ $\qquad$ **(ii)** $y = -\frac{5}{2}x + 9$ $\qquad$ **(b)** $m = \dfrac{3n - 11}{2}$

7. (a) $A(0, 3)$, $B(5, 6)$, $C\left(3\frac{1}{2}, 0\right)$ $\qquad$ **(b)** 18 sq. units

8. (a) $\frac{1}{2}, \frac{1}{2}$ $\qquad$ **(b)** trapezium $\qquad$ **(c)** $E(-1, -1)$ $\qquad$ **(e)** kite

Chapter 5

1. (a) $4\frac{7}{16}$ $\qquad$ **(b)** $x = 4$ or -2

2. (a) $-\frac{1}{2}$ $\qquad$ **(b)** 1 $\qquad$ **(c)** $\frac{4}{11}$

3. (a) $4\frac{1}{4}$ $\qquad$ **(b)** $x = 24$ $\qquad$ **4. (a)** $x = -\frac{3}{2}$ $\qquad$ **(b)** $x = 0$ or 3

5. (a) $x = \dfrac{2}{3}$ or $\dfrac{1}{2}$ (b) $x = \dfrac{-3 \pm \sqrt{6}}{3}$ **6.** $a = 3$ and $b = -1$

7. (a) 8 (b) $x = -3$ **8.** (a) $m = \dfrac{20}{9}$ (b) $n = 2$ or $-\dfrac{1}{2}$

9. (a) $f(x) = 4x$ (b) $f(x) = 2x + 1$ (c) $f(x) = 2x - 5$
(d) $f(x) = x^2 - 1$ (e) $f(x) = 2^x$ (f) $f(x) = 10 - 0.4x$

10. (a) $-\dfrac{2}{5}$ (b) $\dfrac{5}{2}$ (c) $g^{-1}(x) = \dfrac{1 + 3x}{1 + x}$

11. (a) 4 or $-\dfrac{5}{6}$ (b) $x = -2$

12. (a) $f^{-1} : x \to \dfrac{9 - x}{2}$ (b) $g^{-1} : x \to \dfrac{5x + 4}{x}$ (c) $h^{-1} : x \to \dfrac{1}{2x - 3}$

13. $f^{-1}(x) = \dfrac{1 + x}{4x}; \dfrac{3}{4}$ **14.** (a) $g^{-1}(x) = (x - 3)^2 + 4$ (b) 20

15. (a) $-1\dfrac{3}{4}$ (b) 3 or 1 (c) $x = -2$ (d) $x = 3 \pm \sqrt{7}$

16. $a = -7; \dfrac{5}{3}$ **17.** $a = -2, b = 8$ **18.** $a = \dfrac{1}{2}, b = 2$

19. $x = 2$ **20.** $f : x \to \dfrac{2}{x - 3}$ **21.** $f^{-1} : x \to \dfrac{2x}{x + 1}; x = 0$ or 1

22. (a) $y = k\sqrt{x}$ (b) $y = \dfrac{k}{x^3}$ (c) $y = \dfrac{k}{x}$

23. (a) y varies as the square of x (b) y varies inversely as $(x + 3)$
24. (a) $p = 3q^2$ (b) $p = 12$ (c) $q = 4$

25. (a) $y = \dfrac{2}{3}\sqrt[3]{x}$ (b) $x = \dfrac{64}{27}$

26. (a) $y = \dfrac{72}{x^2}$ (b) $y = 288$ (c) $x = \pm 2\sqrt{6}$

27. $p = \dfrac{36}{(q - 2)^2}, q = 14$ or -10 **28.** $m = -8, n = 0$

29. (a) $y = \dfrac{5}{\sqrt{2x - 1}}$ (b) $y = 1$ (c) $x = 113$

30. (a) $k = 72$ (b) $y = 3\sqrt{2}$ **31.** $y = -4$

32. $p = -\dfrac{5}{2}, x = -1$ **33.** $p = 3, y = \dfrac{6}{\sqrt{3x + 3}}, y = \dfrac{2}{3}$

34. (a) $m = 500t^2$ (b) 3.6 cm (c) 3 125 kg
35. (a) 1 658.88 cm^3 (b) 1.5 mm
36. (a) $P = kd$ (b) 480 N/m^2
37. (a) 2 (b) 1 (c) -1

38. (a) $y = 4x^3$ (b) $y = 5\sqrt{x}$ (c) $y = \dfrac{3}{x^2}$

39. $d = 12.5$ **40.** $2\dfrac{1}{2}$ hours **41.** 14 hours

42. $L = 16, 275$ pages **43.** (a) 100 cm (b) 8.0 cm

Chapter 6

1. **(c)** 8.8 **(d)** 1.85 **(e)** 1.2 or –3.2
2. **(a)** –3; –6; 0
   (c) **(i)** – 4.7 **(ii)** 2.6 or –2.1; $(x - 2.6)(x + 2.1) = 0$
   (iii) –6.125, 0.25 **(d)** –1.55, 2.55
3. **(a)** –4; 0; 0 **(c)** $x = -0.5$
   (d) **(i)** $1.25 \leqslant y \leqslant 2.25$ **(ii)** $x > 0.6$ or $x < -1.6$
   (e) **(i)** 1.8 or –2.8 **(ii)** 1.2 or –3.2
4. **(a)** 0; –4.4; –6.9 **(c)** The curve is symmetrical about the origin.
   (d) –2.6, –0.7 **(e)** –2.8, 0, 2.8 **(f)** –7.0
5. **(a)** –1.3; 2.2; 4.1 **(c)** $x > 4.25$ or $x < - 4.25$
   (d) 5.06 sq. units **(e)** 0.75
6. **(a)** $A\left(-\dfrac{1}{2}, 0\right)$, $B(0, 3)$, $C(3, 0)$ **(b)** $x = 1.25$ **(c)** $p \leqslant x \leqslant q$
7. **(a)** 6; –2; –2 **(c)** The curve is symmetrical about the line $x = 3$.
   (d) 1.3, 4.7 **(e)** $0.95 < x < 5.25$ **(f)** 4
8. **(a)** $a = -12$, $b = -6$ **(c)** **(i)** 3.5; –0.2 **(ii)** 3.7, –0.5
   (d) 11 **(e)** 21.3 sq. units **(f)** $x > 3.85$
9. $a = 1\dfrac{1}{2}$, $b = -3\dfrac{1}{2}$, $c = -2$
10. **(a)** 2.9 **(c)** 1.73 **(d)** 1.18 **(e)** $0 < x < 1.12$
11. **(a)** 0, –2, 4 **(c)** **(i)** 1.75 **(ii)** 1.8, –2.8 **(iii)** –0.5
    (iv) –2.25 **(d)** (–2.45, 6.45) and (2.45, 1.55) **(e)** $x = -0.5$
12. **(a)** $a = 18$, $b = -2$, $c = 12$ **(c)** **(i)** 3.1, –0.6 **(ii)** (1.25, –3.1)
    (iii) 0, 2.5 **(iv)** 2.3, 0.2 **(v)** –3 **(d)** $x = 2.4$ or 0.4

Test Paper 3

1. **(a)** $f(x) = \dfrac{1}{4}x$ **(b)** $f(x) = x^3$
2. **(a)** 10 **(b)** 7 **(c)** $-\dfrac{1}{2}$ or 1
3. **(a)** $-\dfrac{5}{3}$ **(b)** $g^{-1}(x) = \dfrac{4 - 7x}{3x}$ **(c)** $\dfrac{1}{3}$ **(d)** $\dfrac{2}{5}$
4. $a = 3$, $b = -7$; $h(-1) = 0$ 5. **(a)** 360 cm^3 **(b)** $6\dfrac{1}{4}$ cm
6. **(a)** 11; 3.5 **(c)** $3.3 < x < 10$ **(d)** –1.3 **(e)** 2.8, 7.2
7. **(a)** $p = 1$, $q = 3.6$ **(c)** **(i)** 3.1 **(ii)** 0.68 **(iii)** 1.72 sq. units
8. **(b)** **(i)** $0 < x < 1.7$ **(ii)** $-0.55 < x < 0.75$ or $x > 2.3$
   (c) –0.85, 0, 2.35

Chapter 7

1. **(a)** 236° **(b)** 293°
2. **(a)** 025°, 090°, 107°, 205° **(b)** 205°, 270°, 287°, 025°
3. **(a)** 21.5° **(b)** 223° **(c)** 137°
4. **(a)** 218° **(b)** 338° **(c)** 083°
5. **(a)** 280° **(b)** 330° **(c)** 100°

6. (a) 100°   (b) 306°   (c) 100°
   (d) 336°   (e) 218°
7. (a) 072°   (b) 108°   (c) 144°   (d) 180°
   (e) 126°   (f) 018°   (g) 234°   (h) 216°
8. (a) 320°   (b) 061°   (c) 122°
9. (a) 264°, 036°, 144°   (b) 084°, 216°, 324°   (c) 294°
10. (a) 207°   (b) 335°   (c) 091°
11. (a) $-\tan 38°$ (b) $-\cos 57°$ (c) $\sin 69°$
   (d) $\cos 81°$ (e) $\tan 78° \sin 89°$ (f) $\sin 15° \cos 24° \tan 33°$
12. (a) 58.0° or 122.0°   (b) 156.3°   (c) 45° or 135°
   (d) 112.6°   (e) 120°   (f) 55° or 125°
   (g) 52°   (h) 29.8°   (i) 99.1°
   (j) 144.7°   (k) 145°
13. (a) $\dfrac{15}{17}$ (b) $-\dfrac{4}{3}$ (c) $-\dfrac{9}{8}$ (d) $\dfrac{10}{17}$
14. (a) 2   (b) (i) $\dfrac{1}{\sqrt{5}}$ (ii) 2   (iii) $-\dfrac{1}{\sqrt{5}}$
15. (a) 5.38   (b) 33.3   (c) 26.4°   (d) 105.4°
   (e) 43.0°   (f) 114.6°   (g) 13.0   (h) 37.5
   (i) 8.90   (j) 21.7   (k) 79.9°
16. (a) 87.5 cm^2 (b) 12.9 cm   (c) 18.1 cm
17. (a) 16.8 cm   (b) 8.95 cm   (c) 8.90 cm
18. (a) 9.66 cm   (b) 9.62 cm   (c) 16.6°
   (d) 145.4°   (e) 11.0 cm^2
19. (a) 145.52   (b) 5.352 cm   (c) 0.371 5   (d) 14.86 cm^2
20. (a) $\dfrac{43}{48}$ (b) $-\dfrac{29}{36}$ 21. (a) $\dfrac{1}{6}$ (b) $\dfrac{8}{11}$
22. (a) (i) 220°   (ii) 340°   (iii) 108.5 m   (iv) 76.60 m
   (b) 214.5 m
23. (a) 2.30 m   (b) 1.11 m^2 (c) 6.21 m^2 (d) 435 m^3
24. 45.0 m
25. (a) 53.1°   (b) 115.6°   (c) 143.1°   (d) 244.4°
26. (a) 107.3 m   (b) 32.5 m   (c) (i) 100°   (ii) 98.5 m
27. (a) 20.6°   (b) 139.4°   (c) 024.7°   (d) 66.8 m
   (e) 64.6 m
28. (a) 080°   (b) 235°   (c) 030°
29. (a) 215°   (b) 4.10 km   (c) 11.0 km
   (d) 6.38 km   (e) 69.0°
30. (a) 21.8°   (b) 90°   (c) 76.8°
31. (a) 12 cm   (b) 12.5 cm   (c) 59.0°
   (d) 42.2°   (e) 53.1°
32. (a) 045°   (b) 225°   (c) 125°   (d) 325°
33. (a) (i) 7.31 km   (ii) 4.70 km   (b) (i) 135°   (ii) 7.07 km

Mid-Term Assessment

Section I

1. (a) 0.002   (b) 7.5×10^{-5} 2. (a) $\dfrac{9 - x}{9 - x^2}$ (b) $x = 0$ or 1

3. (a) 210°   (b) 25%   (c) \$4 500

4. (a) 2   (b) $2\dfrac{1}{16}$ 5. (a) $xy^{\frac{5}{6}}$ (b) $p = \dfrac{1}{3}$

6. (a) $2a(5a + 1)(5a - 1)$ (b) $(7 + x)(1 - 2x)$

7. (a) $x = \dfrac{2p + 3q + 12}{6}$ (b) 2.685 or −0.185

8. (a) $m = 7$ (b) 9, 10, 11

9. (a) $y = \dfrac{2}{\sqrt{x} - 3}$ (b) $x = 103$

10. (a) $2\sqrt{10}$ units   (b) 5   (c) $y = -2x + 6$

Section II

1. (a) (i) 481.5 km to 486.5 km   (ii) 77 km to 83 km

    (b) 459.9 cm³   (c) $\dfrac{4}{5} < x \leqslant 4$

2. (a) (i) $-a^2$ (ii) $y = ax - a^2$ (c) $y = 3x - 9$ or $y = 2x - 4$

3. (a) 127.4°   (b) 26.6 cm, 32.8 cm²

4. (a) 36   (b) 5   (c) $3 + \sqrt{x}$ (d) $x = 4.5$

5. (a) 0; 4   (c) (i) $x = -1.8, -0.2$ and 1.8   (ii) 4 sq. units

    (d) −2.3

Chapter 8

1. (a) $x = 64, y = 58$ (b) $x = 24, y = 136$

2. (a) $x = 32, y = 58, z = 58$ (b) $x = 3, y = 5.82, z = 59$

3. (a) 40°   (b) 1.43 cm   (c) 7.25 cm

4. (a) $x = 8, y = 6$ (b) $314\dfrac{2}{7}$ cm²

5. (a) 4 cm   (b) 10 cm   (c) 30.72 cm²

6. (a) $x = 58, y = 58$ (b) $x = 118, y = 62$ (c) $x = 61, y = 59.5$

    (d) $x = 76, y = 38$ (e) $x = 63, y = 121.5$ (f) $x = 153, y = 36$

7. $x = 110, y = 70$ 8. $x = 84, y = 102$ 9. $x = 32.5, y = 97.5$

Chapter 9

1. (a) 27°   (b) 68°   (c) 44°

2. (a) 124°   (b) 95°   3. (a) 117°   (b) 80°

4. (a) 56°   (b) 112°   (c) 28°

5. (a) 97°   (b) 80°

6. (a) 72°   (b) 76°   (c) 108°

7. (a) 38°   (b) 52°   (c) 26°   (d) 116°

8. **(a)** 22° **(b)** 23° **9.** $x = 90, y = 136$
10. **(a)** $x = 35, y = 8$ **(b)** $x = 74, y = 148, z = 42$
11. **(a)** $x = 66, y = 42$ **(b)** $x = 26, y = 73$
12. **(a)** 62° **(b)** 34°
13. $x = 108, y = 126$ **14.** $x = 79, y = 62$ **15.** $x = 44, y = 21$
16. **(a)** $x = 53, y = 53$ **(b)** $x = 20, y = 98$
17. **(a)** $x = 78, y = 65$ **(b)** $x = 62, y = 33$

Test Paper 4
1. **(a)** $x = 61, y = 30.5$ **(b)** $x = 32.5, y = 65$
2. **(a)** 30° **(b)** 8 cm **(c)** 6.93 cm
3. $x = 70, y = 58$ **4.** $x = 35, y = 62$
5. **(a)** $x = 44, y = 68$ **(b)** $x = 32, y = 58$ **6.** **(a)** 7.5 cm
    (b) **(i)** 8.24 cm **(ii)** 11.8 cm **(iii)** 4.91 cm
    (c) **(i)** 16 cm **(ii)** 67.4° **(iii)** 122.4 cm^2
7. **(a)** $x = 45, y = 135$ **(b)** $x = 30, y = 56$

Chapter 10, 11

1.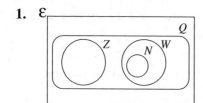

2.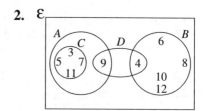

3.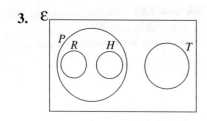

4.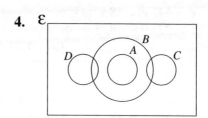

5.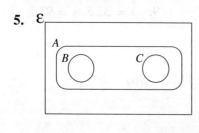

6.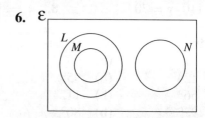

(a) B **(b)** A **(a)** { } **(b)** M
(c) N **(d)** L

7. **(a)** 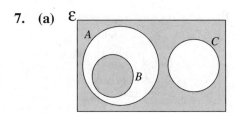 **(b)**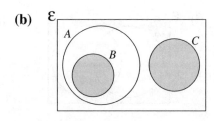

8. **(a)** 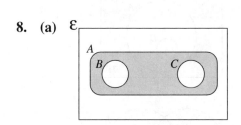 **(b)**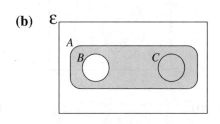

(c) 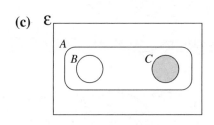 **(d)**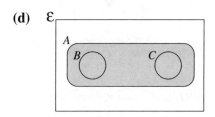

9. **(a)** 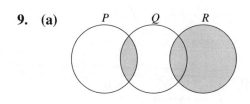 **(b)**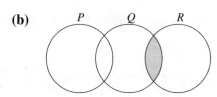

(c) 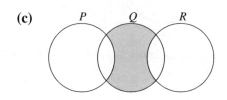 **(d)**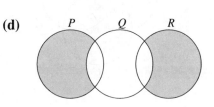

10.

(a) $A \cap B'$	**(b)** $A' \cup B$	**(c)** $A \cap B'$
(d) $A' \cup B$	**(e)** $A \cap (B \cup C)$	**(f)** $A \cup (B \cap C)$
(g) $A \cap B \cap C'$	**(h)** $(A \cup B)' \cap C$	**(i)** $(A \cap B) \cup C'$
(j) $(A \cap B)' \cup C$		

11. **(a)** **(i)** 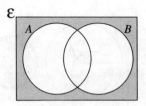 **(ii)**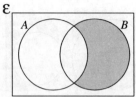

(b) **(i)** 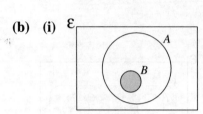 **(ii)**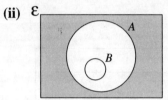

(c) **(i)** 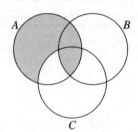 **(ii)**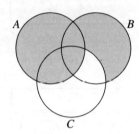

(iii) 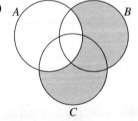 **(iv)**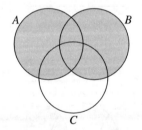

(v) 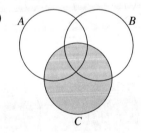 **(vi)**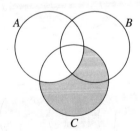

(vii) 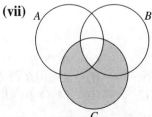 **(viii)**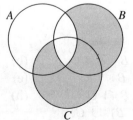

12. (a) (i) 1   (ii) 2
     (b) (i) {*l*}   (ii) {*f, i, j*}
14. (a) (i) {3, 6, 7, 14}
     (ii) {12, 13, 14, 15, 16, 17}
     (iii) {3, 6, 7}
     (b) (i) 6   (ii) 5

13.

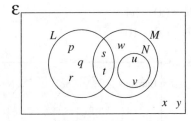

{*s, t, u, v*}

     (b) (i) 24   (ii) 16
         (iii) 48   (iv) 64
         (v) 84   (vi) 76

15. (a)

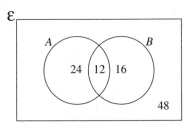

16. (a) (i) {12, 24}   (ii) {10, 11, 13, 14, 17, 19, 22, 23}
     (b) (i) 2   (ii) φ
17. (a)

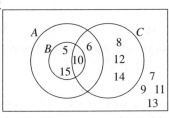

     (b) (i) {5, 6, 8, 10, 12, 14, 15}
         (ii) 7

18. (a) {1, 2, 4, 6, 8, 9, 10, 12, 14, 16, 18} (b) 7
19. (a) 20, 0   (b) 65, 45
20. (a) (i) 13, 24   (ii) 0, 11
     (b) (i) 5   (ii) 6
21. (a) 16   (b) (i) 5   (ii) 63   (iii) 6
22.

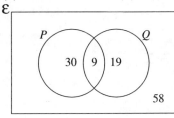

23. (a) 4
     (b) 20

24. (a) (i) 5   (ii) 5   (b)

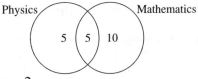

25.

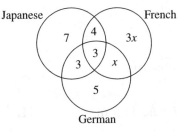

     (a) $x = 2$
     (b) 15
     (c) 6

26. (a) 34   **(b)** 63

27. (a) 10   **(b)** 21

28.

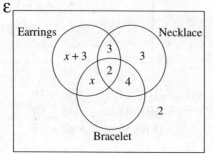

(a) $x = 3$

(b) 7

(c) 12

29. (a) 7   **(b)** 2   **(c)** 9

Chapter 12

1. (a) (i) 5 m/s   **(ii)** 0 m/s   **(iii)** 10 m/s   **(b)** 35 m
    (c) 3.5 m/s   **(d)** The object was stationary and its speed was zero.

2. (a) (i) 5 m/s^2 **(ii)** 0 m/s^2 **(iii)** -10 m/s^2
    (b) 157.5 m   **(c)** 15.75 m/s
    (d) The acceleration of the object was zero as it was moving with constant speed.

3. 26.4 km/h   **4. (a)** 12   **(b)** 2.5 m/s   **(c)** 1.54 m/s

5. (a) 2.5 m/s^2 **(b)** 4   **(c)** 18

6.

$1\frac{3}{7}$ m/s^2, $\frac{1}{3}$ m/s^2, 187 m

7. (a) (i) 50 s   **(ii)** 5 m/s   **(iii)** 4 m/s   **(iv)** 5 m/s

    (b)

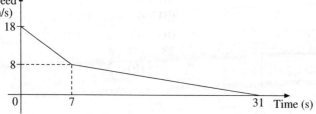

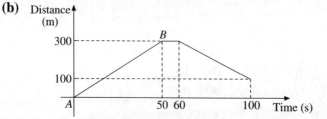

8. $-\frac{4}{3}$ m/s^2 **9.** 0.8 m/s^2, 360 m   **10.** 17 m/s, 47.5 m   **11.** 30 s

12. (a)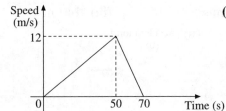
Speed (m/s)

12

0   50 70   Time (s)

(b) (i) 0.24 m/s² **(ii)** 420 m

13. (a) 5 s **(b)** 3

14. (a) Speed (m/s)

30

0   20 32 42   Time (s)

(b) (i) –3 m/s² **(ii)** 23.18 m/s

15. (a) Speed (m/s)

10

4

0   2   4   6   Time (s)

(b) (i) 2 m/s² **(ii)** 26 m

16. (a) Speed (m/s)

24

15   t   25

0   Time (s)

(b) 90 s **17.** 70 s

18. (a) Speed (m/s)

max speed

0   T   70   Time (s)

(b) $T = 50$, max speed $= 30$ m/s

19. (a) $T = 3$ **(b) (i)** 2.4 m/s² **(c)** 288 m
20. (a) $u = 21$ **(b)** 0.75 m/s²
(c) (i) 15 m/s **(ii)** 12 m/s **(d)** 645 m

21. (a) (i) $\frac{2}{3}$ m/s² **(ii)** 12 m/s **(b)** 35

22. (a) (i) 2 m/s²   **(ii)** 8 m/s   **(iii)** 240 m

(b) (i) Distance (m) graph   **(ii)** Acceleration (m/s²) graph

23. (a) 40 m/s   **(b)** 30 s   **(c)** 1.8 km

24. (a) $43\frac{1}{3}$ m/s   **(b)** $\frac{4}{3}$ m/s²   **(c)** 40

25. (a) (i) 40 m/s   **(ii)** 1 000 m   **(b)** 18

26. (a) 0.85 m/s²   **(b)** 10.1 m/s   **(c)** 270 m

27. (a) (i) 22 m/s   **(ii)** $3\frac{2}{3}$ m/s²   **(b)** 20 s

28. (a) $\frac{2}{3}$ m/s²   **(b)** 525 m   **(c)** 10 m/s

(d) 6 or 38   **(e)** 24 m/s

29. (a) 20 min   **(b)** 72 km/h   **(c)** 86 km   **(d)** 44 km/h

30. (a) 12   **(b)** 10.4 km/h

(c) Distance (km) vs Time (s) graph showing 1st cyclist and 2nd cyclist

(d) About 17 km from X

31. (a) (i) $1\frac{1}{3}$ m/s²   **(ii)** 30 m/s   **(b) (i)** 60   **(ii)** 1 050 m

Test Paper 5

1. (a)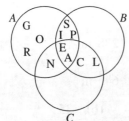

(b) (i) 5

(ii) 15

(c) (i) {E, A}

(ii) {A, C, E, L, N, I, P, S}

(d) B

2.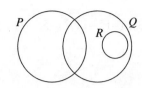

3. (a) $x = 32$, $y = 7$ **(b)** 29   **(c)** 78

4. (a) 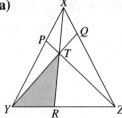   **(b)**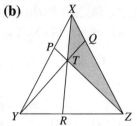

5. (a) 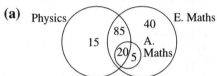   **(b)** 15

                                                (c) 165

6. (a)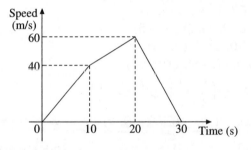

(b) 60 m/s   **(c)** 6 m/s^2

7. (a) 1.2 m/s^2 **(b)** 135 m   **(d)** 22.8 m/s

(e)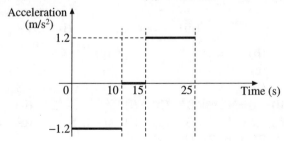

8. (a) 85   **(b)** 20   **(c)** 420 m   **(d)** 32

Chapter 13

1. (a) (i) (0, 1), (1, 1), (2, –2)   **(ii)** (–1, 0), (–1, 1), (2, 2)

     (b) (i) (0, 1), (0, 3), (–2, 4), (–2, 0)   **(ii)** (7, –4), (5, –4), (4, –6), (8, –6)

(c) **(i)** $\left(\frac{1}{2}, 0\right)$, $\left(\frac{1}{2}, 1\right)$, $\left(1, \frac{1}{2}\right)$ **(ii)** (−1, −3), (−1, −11), (−5, −7)

(d) **(i)** (2, −3), $\left(2\frac{1}{2}, -2\right)$, (3, −1), $\left(3\frac{1}{2}, -2\right)$

     (ii) (3, 1), $\left(3\frac{1}{2}, 2\right)$, (4, 3), $\left(4\frac{1}{2}, 2\right)$

(e) **(i)** (0, 0), (1, 0), (3, 2), (4, 2)   **(ii)** (0, 0), (1, 3), (1, 5), (0, 2)
(f) **(i)** (2, 1), (6, 1), (6, 2), (4, 2), (4, 3), (2, 3)

     (ii) $\left(1, \frac{1}{2}\right)$, $\left(3, \frac{1}{2}\right)$, (3, 1), (2, 1), $\left(2, 1\frac{1}{2}\right)$, $\left(1, 1\frac{1}{2}\right)$

2. $a = 5$, $b = 5$, $c = -4$, $d = -3$
3.   **(a)** (−5, 1)   **(b)** (8, −4)
4.   **(a)** **(i)** $A'(3, 0)$, $B'(0, 4)$, $C'(-1, 3)$, $D'(-2, -3)$
         (ii) $A'(-3, 0)$, $B'(0, -4)$, $C'(1, -3)$, $D'(2, 3)$
         (iii) $A'(-1, 0)$, $B'(2, -4)$, $C'(3, -3)$, $D'(4, 3)$
         (iv) $A'(3, -4)$, $B'(0, 0)$, $C'(-1, -1)$, $D'(-2, -7)$
         (v) $A'(0, 3)$, $B'(-4, 0)$, $C'(-3, -1)$, $D'(3, -2)$
         (vi) $A'(3, 0)$, $B'(7, 3)$, $C'(6, 4)$, $D'(0, 5)$
    (b) **(i)** $A'(0, -3)$, $B'(-4, 0)$, $C'(-3, 1)$, $D'(3, 2)$
         (ii) $A'(2, 1)$, $B'(-2, 2)$, $C'(-1, 3)$, $D'(5, 4)$
         (iii) $A'(5, -2)$, $B'(8, 2)$, $C'(9, 1)$, $D'(10, -5)$
    (c) **(i)** $A'(4, 5)$, $B'(1, 1)$, $C'(0, 2)$, $D'(-1, 8)$
         (ii) $A'(5, -5)$, $B'(2, -9)$, $C'(1, -8)$, $D'(0, -2)$

    (d) **(i)** $A'\left(-1\frac{1}{2}, 0\right)$, $B'(0, 2)$, $C'\left(\frac{1}{2}, 1\frac{1}{2}\right)$, $D'\left(1, -1\frac{1}{2}\right)$

         (ii) $A'(5, 0)$, $B'(-4, -12)$, $C'(-7, -9)$, $D'(-10, 9)$

5.   **(a)** **(i)** $x = -\frac{1}{2}$ **(ii)** $y = -3$ **(iii)** $y = x - 5$ **(iv)** $3x + y = 0$

    (b) **(i)** $x = \frac{1}{2}$ **(ii)** $y = 3$ **(iii)** $y = x + 5$ **(iv)** $3x + y = 0$

    (c) **(i)** $x = -\frac{1}{2}$ **(ii)** $y = -1$ **(iii)** $y = x - 3$ **(iv)** $3x + y = 2$

6.   **(a)** $x = 0$ **(b)** $y = x$ **(c)** $y = -x$
    (d) $x = 5$ **(e)** $y = -2$ **(f)** $y = -x$
7.   **(a)** $y = -2$ **(b)** $y = 1$ **(c)** $y = -x + 3$
8.   **(a)** **(i)** $y = x - 3$ **(ii)** $y = -2x + 8$ **(b)** **(i)** $y = x - 2$ **(ii)** $y = -2x$
9.   **(a)**   (1, −3)   **(b)** $x = 1$, $y = 3$ **(c)** **(i)**   (−4, 5)   **(ii)**   (−6, −1)
10.   **(a)** $B(3, 0)$, $C(3, 2)$, $D(1, 2)$, $P(6, 2)$, $Q(4, 2)$
    (b) **(i)**   4 sq. units   **(ii)**   3 sq. units
11.   **(a)** AB **(b)** $A(2, 2)$, $C(6, 4)$, $D(2, 4)$, $Q(4, 4)$ **(c)**   8 sq. units
12.   **(a)** AB **(b)**   (5, 2)   **(c)**   3 sq. units
13.   **(a)** **(i)** OB **(ii)**   (3, 6)
    (b)   H is a shear with OA as the invariant line segment such that B moves 3 units to B'. M is a reflection in the line $x = 1\frac{1}{2}$.

(c) 12 sq. units   **(d) (i)** O **(ii)** $(3, 4)$ **(iii)** 6 sq. units

14. (a) $A'(3, 0), B'(9, 0), C'(3, 2)$; 6 sq. units

     (b) $A'(1, 0), B'(3, 0), C'(1, 3)$; 3 sq. units

15. (a) $A'(5, 0), B'(3, 4), C'(6, 10)$; A **(b)** $A'\left(\dfrac{5}{3}, 0\right), B'(1, 2), C'(2, 5)$

16. (a) An anticlockwise rotation of $90°$ about the origin O.

     (b) A reflection in the line $y = -x$.

     (c) A shear with A as the invariant point and which moves B and C 4 units parallel to the y-axis.

     (d) A stretch parallel to the x-axis with factor $2\dfrac{1}{2}$.

17. H is a shear with O as the invariant point such that A and B move 4 units to the right parallel to the x-axis. M is a reflection in the x-axis.

18. (f) $\triangle ABC = \triangle A_1 B_1 C_1 = \triangle A_2 B_2 C_2 = \triangle AB_4 C$ = 4 sq. units

Chapter 14

1. (a)

Score	Tally mark	Midpt. (x)	Frequency (f)	fx
1 – 10		5.5	0	0
11 – 20	//	15.5	2	31
21 – 30	//	25.5	2	51
31 – 40	//	35.5	2	71
41 – 50	⫰⫰⫰ /	45.5	6	273
51 – 60	⫰⫰⫰ /	55.5	6	333
61 – 70	⫰⫰⫰ //	65.5	7	458.5
71 – 80	⫰⫰⫰ ///	75.5	8	604
81 – 90	⫰⫰⫰ /	85.5	6	513
91 – 100	/	95.5	1	95.5
			$\Sigma f = 40$	$\Sigma fx = 2\,430$

     (c) 15

     (d) (i) 60.75   **(ii)** 71 – 80   **(iii)** 61 – 70

2. (b) 70 – 80

3. (a) 12, 10, 8   **(b)** 60   **(c)** 22.375 hours

4. (a)

Score	10	20	30	40	50	60	70	80	90	100
No. of students with this score or less	0	2	4	6	12	18	25	33	39	40

(c) (i) 47 (ii) 76 (iii) 63 (iv) 29
(d) 54 (e) 11
6. (a) 37, 82, 129, 157, 173
7. (a) $3 (b) $1 (c) 66 (d) 37
(e) $a = 30$, $b = 30$, $c = 10$
8. (a) 9, 21, 43, 185 (c) (i) 82 km/h (ii) 16 km/h (iii) 17
(d) 39

Test Paper 6
1. (a) $C(2, 3)$, $D(0, 3)$, $Q(4, 3)$
   (b) (i) A stretch parallel to the x-axis with factor 2 and the y-axis as the invariant line.
   (ii) A reflection in the line BC.
   (iii) A translation 2 units in the x-direction.
   (iv) A clockwise rotation of 90° about B.
   (v) A shear with AB as the invariant line segment and which moves C 2 units to the right parallel to AB.
2. (c) (ii) $x + y = -4$ (d) (i) (4, 1) (ii) -2 (iii) $1 : 4$
   (g) (ii) 90°; (0, 0) (iii) (a) A reflection in the x-axis.
   (iii) (b) A translation -6 units in the y-direction.
3. (a) 3.7 km (b) 1.3 km (c) 28 (d) $a = 4$, $b = 14$, $c = 3$
4. (a) 6 (b) 54 (d) $6 - 8$ (e) 7.72 cm
5. (a) 4.8 cm (b) 38; 62; 74
   (d) (i) 70.5 years (ii) 14.5 years (iii) 11

Final Term Assessment

Section I
1. (a) 5.12×10^{-7} (b) 1.25×10^2
2. (a) 221.1 (b) 0.699 3
3. $\dfrac{a + b}{a^2}$, $\dfrac{2}{3}$ 4. $\dfrac{23}{32}$
5. (a) $k = 2\ 000$ (b) $y = 16$ (c) 0.8
6. (a) $A(-2, 0)$, $B(0, 6)$, $C(3, 0)$

   (b) $x = \dfrac{1}{2}$ (c) $x < -2$ or $x > 3$
7. (a) 50° (b) 60° (c) 40° (d) 35°
8. (a) 30 s (b) $v = \dfrac{3}{2}x$ (c) $d = 15y - 75$ (d) 54 km/h
9. (a) A (b) $C(4, 4)$, $B'(6, 4)$, $M'(4, 2)$ (c) 12 sq. units
10. (a) (i) 5.706 cm^2 (ii) 1.236 cm
    (b) (i) 078° (ii) 288° (iii) 136°

Section II

1. (a) (i)

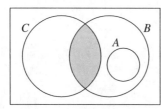

(ii)

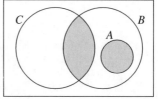

(iii)

(b) (i) 2 **(ii)** C

(c) Burger-A, Burger-C, regions labelled 9, $11-x$, $2x$, x, 5, $x+1$, 9, Burger-B

(i) $x = 5$
(ii) 22
(iii) 50%

2. (a) (i) 14.0° **(ii)** 83.4°
(b) (i) 16.1 km **(ii)** 10.6 km **(iii)** 182°

3. (b) (i) 90° **(ii)** $(-8, 4)$
(iii) A clockwise rotation of 90° about the point $(6, 2)$.
(c) $y = -x$

4. (a) (i) $\{3, 4, 5, 6, 7\}$ **(ii)** $\{3, 10\}$ **(iii)** $\{8, 9\}$ **(iv)** $\{3, 8, 9, 10\}$

(b) (i) $AB = (x + 2)$ cm, $AR = \left(\dfrac{20}{x + 2} - 1 \right)$ cm **(iii)** 3.10 cm or 12.90 cm

5. (a) (i)

Marks	No. of candidates
10 marks or less	2
20 marks or less	8
30 marks or less	17
40 marks or less	24
50 marks or less	44
60 marks or less	76
70 marks or less	106
80 marks or less	130
90 marks or less	144
100 marks or less	150

(iii) (a) 58 **(b)** 28 **(c)** 15
(b) (ii) 65 – 70